Love on the Edge

MINDFUL WRITERS RETREAT SERIES

Foreword by **KATHLEEN SHOOP**
Edited by **DEMI STEVENS**
Mindful Writers Retreat Authors

"Finn & Chloe," "Ebby & Oscar"– Kathleen Shoop
"Love on the Edge" – Kimberly Kurth Gray
"A Minute-Long Love" – Hilary Hauck
"For Cheeku," "Oh, Wow!" "To My Husband" – Madhu Bazaz Wangu
"When to Drop the L-Bomb" – James Robinson, Jr.
"Just Give It Seven Days" – Amy Morley
"Astaria's Tooth Fairy Adventure" – MaryAlice Meli
"Always and Forever," "Love Is" – Judy England-McCarthy
"Love at the B&B" – Michele Savaunah Zirkle
"Precious Jewel" – Demi Stevens
"Angelica" – Lorraine Donohue Bonzelet
"My Beloved" – Jennifer D. Diamond
"Where It's Needed Most" – Phil Giunta
"The Surprise" – Lisa Valli
"Sassy Sera" – N. J. Hammer
"Fire and Ice" – Kim Pierson
"The Love Riddle," "The Hi-Fi Needle" – Gail Oare
"Red Sky" – Abigail Drake
"The Elephant in the Room" – Deborah Vita
"What is Love?" – S. M. Kraftchak
"When Food is Love" – Ramona DeFelice Long
"Recipe for Love" – Denise Weaver

Mindful Writers Retreat Series
135 Glen Avenue
Glen Rock, PA 17327

Print ISBN: 978-1-64649-189-6
Ebook ISBN: 978-1-64649-190-2

CONTENTS

FOREWORD

L ove. According to Merriam-Webster's definition, to love is to hold something or someone dear, to desire actively, to thrive in the midst of it, because of it. It's also defined and experienced as a noun—to feel great affection for things or people. People can be in love, be loving, lose love, make love, commit to the hard work of long-term love. And as you read the variety of stories, poems, and essays collected in *Love on the Edge* you'll submerge into worlds that reveal the unique ways love shows up. The collection offers fun, witty, touching, poignant, and insightful pieces—something for everyone, for every mood.

These short stories take you back in time for historical renderings of love in the time of war—relationships that have to wait for a soldier's return to even begin. Contemporary pieces depict the wonder of love at first sight and long walks in the snow, attraction sparked by shared television show references, passion helped and hindered by nosy neighbors, a nudge in the right direction from a pesky ghost, amusing, modern takes on the first blush of mature love, fairy friends, an empath's struggle to save others and flourish himself, the last breath of love, a magical botanic romance, and first love when a world in crises has sent communities into hiding just to survive.

⸴ Edge features nonfiction and poetry that
⸴ɪe very use of the word love, the evolution of
ɪess inside of marriage, the adoration of
ɪchildren and grandparents, pets, rivers, and food.
ɔd, the essence of life and love, reveals its power
ɪhrough devotion and keeping memories close.

While the feeling of love can be life-giving and its loss can devastate, it is the act of loving that is a force for good and change. Nowhere is the act of love more needed than in the area of mental health for children and families. As with all of the Mindful Writers Retreat Anthologies, this collection benefits an organization. Monies raised through sales of *Love on the Edge* are donated to the Allegheny Children's Initiative—Partners For Quality, Inc.

While most diseases and conditions are easily diagnosed and treated, mental illness lies invisible in a child, but can be every bit as destructive as cancer or organ failure. Allegheny Children's Initiative works in holistic ways to treat both child and family. Talented, invested case-workers support them in the home and in conjunction with other mental health partners. The donations from the anthology may be small compared to what is needed, but hopefully the overt act of love for people who are often overlooked will have an impact beyond our imagination.

And this brings us to the person this collection is dedicated to—Ramona DeFelice Long—someone who fully understood the power of overt acts of love. A mindful writer in every sense, Ramona is missed by her writing community every day. A gifted author, Ramona brought history to life, creating a mother and daughter attempting to reconcile their past in *The Murderess of Bayou Rosa*. She delicately revealed the deeply rooted ache when a sister witnesses a brother's pain in her Pushcart nominated story, "Voices." She explored ways dying shaped living in "Acorns," and so much more in so many other writings.

Ramona was a champion for the careworn writer, editing manuscripts with precision and candor. She delighted in the trappings of the Royals and all things deemed fashionable by the world even if not by her. And she valued the ways life was complicated. She grasped that bad things could happen to good people, that pain and loss and unrealized ambitions shaped one's path as much as joy and success, but that it was all part of living. She was always the first to rush in to assist those who needed more or needed "differently."

Though she drew healthy boundaries, Ramona was never too busy to connect and listen. She wasn't a therapist or healthcare practitioner, but she empathized with the baffling unfolding of life in its fragile and miraculous ways and mirrored back one's strength in order to boost, to love. Her understanding of the human condition was a gift to all who knew her. She is the embodiment of why writers write. Her family and friends will remember her forever in various ways, but as years tick by, her writings will carry her wisdom on love and life and living to new readers, to those who need her voice.

Enjoy this anthology! It really is a wonderful, uplifting collection. It expresses all the things about life that make it worth living. Especially when joy and bliss come peeking through periods of discontent, just the way Ramona liked it. And exactly like that, love's impact is ever present in good times and bad.

—Kathleen Shoop

FINN & CHLOE

Kathleen Shoop

Once upon a time a guy sat in a bar. Stood up, mortified, unmoored. Finn Corbett's perfect life had been balled up and tossed into the garbage like a plane spiraled out of the sky when its engine gave out. He sighed then downed the rest of his Iron City Light, glancing around the Three Rivers Tavern. Had anyone noticed the fat bouquet of ranunculus sitting beside him like it was his Valentine date? He'd gone to three florists on his postal route to find the right combination of every shade of pink and red colors that ValentineDreamer2 had said would melt her heart.

Turns out she was heartless, leaving a guy to stew in his ranunculus juices after sounding so excited to meet him. He checked his watch. Over an hour late. The lights dimmed, the dancefloor filled, and the band cranked out its first moody love song. Time to escape. He slid a twenty for a $4.50 beer under the bottle and stuffed the bouquet into his mail bag. Slipping out of the booth, trying to stay as small as possible, he jiggled the table, knocking the bottle off. A waitress breezed past, scooping it up just before it hit the floor. She set it on the table and bent down. "Um, your flowers." She straightened bearing a couple of stems.

Pulling up to his full six feet four height, his hairline pricked with sweat.

"They tumbled out of your bag there... oh..." she brushed the blooms with her fingertips. "Like velvet. Ranunculus. A lucky la-dy..." her voice trailed off when she looked back at the table and realized there was no lady. She shoved them toward him. "They're beautiful."

"Keep 'em."

Her face brightened, but before she said more, a customer called her away. Finn pulled his bag-strap over his shoulder and balked, the shocking pain reminding him he'd never get back on the pitcher's mound if he didn't baby it a little. Switching the bag to his other shoulder he limped, dismayed. He stopped and lifted his foot. What had he done to it? The leap over the fence when the Rottweiler chased him? The slip off the wet curb when the downpour kept Mrs. Renfrew on her porch with a letter she'd forgotten to add to the box?

He shook his head. Five months since he'd been released by the minor-league baseball team, Altoona Curve. There was only one way back to making his dream come true and that was to be fully healthy. Turns out, being cut from Double-A ball, having no savings or health insurance, made that harder to do than most would expect. But then his luck shifted, just a little tiny bit, like the sun splitting through dark clouds and an ump saying "Play ball," he found the job as a postal carrier in Pittsburgh.

It had been perfect. His route kept him moving, he had the energy to work out and do physical therapy in the evening and the job paid that bill. All seemed to be going in the right direction until that night there in the tavern when his aloneness sat heavy as a just-filled mailbag.

Weaving through dancing couples toward the exit, he considered that he'd never been stood up before, not once in his entire life. Perhaps he should have added the fact he had been (and soon would be again, he just knew it) a professional baseball player to his profile, and ValentineDreamer2 would be nesting the ranunculus in her arms that very moment.

But then he'd have to explain the whole system, why he wasn't playing right then. It was true, very few people understood the competition in Double-A ball was often better than Triple-A... oh, there he went again. How often did he talk about baseball? Maybe ValentineDreamer2 could sense it through the internet, his self-centeredness sucking away all the energy in the room. Wasn't that what Sarah had always said to him? Yep. He shook his head as he wove through the Valentine lovers, arms looped around necks, as bodies melded on the dance floor. Perhaps his loneliness had settled in long before he admitted it that night. Perhaps he was getting just what he deserved.

Chloe Marshall teetered around the living room in vintage peek-a-boo high heels and a magenta, peek-a-boo dress that cut tight along the bodice then flared, adorned with a thousand organza butterflies, lifting the skirt when she spun. She checked her watch—another vintage piece her mother had found for her years back, before she died. Chloe might be a few minutes late for the date but she hoped to get there just in time.

"Now that's a pretty dress," Chloe's father said. He hobbled into the room, one hand shaking as his fingers gripped his cane, the other hand wrapped around a can of Iron City Beer as his gait grew into a limp.

"Daddy." She kicked off her heels and rushed to his side to steady him as he completed the path to his recliner. She pulled the side table closer to his chair and set his beer on a coaster the way her mom had liked. She straightened his glasses on his nose and handed him the remote. "You'll be the death of me."

"Well, at least in death you'll have to get out of the house then, right?"

She spread her arms. "Look at me. I'm headed out. I promised." It would be the first date she'd been on since her boyfriend proposed on Instagram.

To another woman.

The humiliation had been suffocating. The blurry recording of the proposal and the boyfriend's choice in fiancée who'd been built like Chloe and had the same long, golden hair that hung in thick curls, meant friend after friend called to offer best wishes. Later that week, when her father had the stroke, well, she left California and returned home to Pittsburgh to nurse her father, her wounds, and to figure out how to start her life all over again.

Ed Marshall held the remote in two hands, strangling the buttons so tight the device shook.

"Here." Chloe took the remote. "What channel is the Pirates game on?"

"KDKA?"

She shook her head. "Look at your list. It's a rerun, Daddy. It's February. Remember."

He put a finger in the air. "Spring training soon."

"Yep, soon." She called up the cable menu. "I think the replays are on MLB or... ESPN..."

"Damn channels. I can't keep up."

"You're doing fine, Dad."

She found the pregame show leading into a game that was played thirty years before. Her father pulled the clock from the side table onto his lap and wound it. For good luck he always turned his clock behind an hour to the time the game started when he won a national championship in college. It was a strange superstition that he'd kept up since he was twenty years old. It was no use to reason with him that the power of a superstition, even if it worked when he played, wouldn't just slide over to another team in another era, decades later. And it certainly wouldn't work on a game already played.

"Do you need anything before I go?"

He looked up at her, his brown eyes warm and loving, turned down at the outside corners.

"That's where he used to pitch 'em," her mother would brag. *"Low and just outside enough to hit the strike-zone and leave batters lookin'. I love those sweet eyes."*

And Luna Marshall had. Chloe's parents shared a great love that only made the absence of it in her life more stark, more painful.

"Got all I need," her father said. "'Cept for the fact that the fella isn't picking you up here."

"Oh, no. I don't want him to know where I live."

"Well, I don't like it."

"I know you don't."

"You need someone."

"I'm looking for someone like you, Dad. Makes it sort of impossible."

"Hmmph." He looked back at the TV, sinking into the recliner, and she knew he'd be safe, comfortable, and happy for a couple of hours.

On her way out, Chole pulled on her faux-fur cape, and glanced in the mirror. She'd gone through a lot of trouble to make herself look the way she used to like to, to make herself feel like her old self again. And in that moment, she did. Another look at her watch and off she went into a gray sky that had started dropping silver dollar sized snowflakes.

Outside the Three Rivers Tavern, Finn dug through his bag, fingers brushing past the ranunculus, searching. There it was, a lump at the bottom—the wallet he'd been charged with returning just before he finished his shift. His friend, Matty Gershon, had been held up on his route and asked Finn to finish up the letters and take the wallet back to the post office where it could be bundled in an envelope and returned to the address found inside. But Finn had been bent on finding the exact flowers his date said she loved and he ran out of time to get the wallet where it needed to go. Late for the date. Late for nothing, it turned out. Would he ever find someone... someone who... someone just right? Not wanting to go sit alone in a barely furnished apartment, he decided to forgo taking the wallet to the post office and instead decided to return it right then.

Finn moved under the streetlamp for better light and opened the wallet. No credit cards, no license, no health insurance card, no library card. He fanned through the cash, ten twenties, and found a slip of paper with an address. He hoped the address was for the owner and not just some person the owner knew. It was a start at least. And with the way his night had gone, if he could help someone out, it'd be worth it.

Starting to snow, the white flakes glistened in the streetlight, making Finn smile. While he loved the idea of his shoulder healing enough to go to Florida for spring training, he loved a good snow. And so he headed toward Mulberry Street hoping that the return of the wallet would pull his evening out of the gutter.

Chloe stepped inside Three Rivers Tavern and shook the snow off her cape. She put it over her arm, checked the time and edged further inside.

"Can I help you?" the hostess asked.

"Ummm." She poked her head into the main bar where people were draped in each other's arms on the dance floor, seated at tables for two, heads bowed in intimate conversation and... Oh. There he was. HighBall7. He'd said he was tall with brown hair and that he'd have his work bag with him. This man fit the criteria. She turned back to the hostess. "I think I've got it covered."

And she drew a deep breath, sauntered across the room, and leaned against the bar. "Hi," she said. The man drew his gaze up and down her body.

"Heyyyyy. Oh..." He leaned toward her. "Heyyyyy."

She drew back. His grizzled five o'clock shadow, slurred speech and scent of having drank all day confused her. This couldn't be the man she'd spoken to. Not that they'd spoken, actually. She'd been working from her laptop since her phone was being repaired, and well, now she felt ridiculous for reading anything into the man's nature from a few lines about how he wanted someone to share in staving off the cold draft of a Valentine's Day alone. *Staving?* This man with his half-closed eyes certainly didn't look like a man who'd use the word stave on a dating site.

Chloe sighed, shoulders slumped. She scanned the bar for signs of anyone else alone. Anyone who resembled the man in the photo. *Nope.* Oh, well. This was just what she should have expected with her bad luck. And she bundled her cape over her shoulders and started toward the exit, into the snow, hoping it might blanket her with all the comfort she'd never find in a man.

Chole reached home, having decided to walk even though the snow dumped down fat and fast. She opened the picket gate and started up the walk when she noticed. Something was off. The front door was open, and golden light from inside sprayed out onto the porch. Her mouth went dry and her hands shook. *Dad?* He was vulnerable and... she never should have left him.

She bounded through the front door and stopped as soon as she crossed the threshold to the living room. "Dad?" She grasped the door jamb with one hand.

He looked up and smiled. "Chloe."

"Dad."

"Look who I found for you."

She rushed to his side and got down to eye level. "Are you all right?" She ran her hands over his arms, patting his shoulder as though she was waking him from sleep.

He swatted her hands away. "'Course. Look."

She glanced at the person sitting next to him then did a double-take. A handsome dark-haired man, just perched there as if he swung by the house every day for visits with her father. She squinted at him. A handsome burglar? Her gaze darted around the room, settling on the bag beside him. Pink, magenta, and blush and lipstick red and cranberry hued ranunculus stuck out of a postal bag. Confused, she stood. It had to be him. But no.

"It's you," he said, sliding to the edge of the chair.

She shook her head. It was him. "You stood me up," she said.

"You stood me up," he said.

"No."

"I waited over an hour... for ValentineDreamer2. You are her?"

"You're HighBall7? Like the drink?"

"Like the pitch," he said.

Chloe's dad looked back and forth between them.

"The pitch? Is that like a line you give all the girls before you stand them up?"

"I waited. I was on time—"

"I was on time," she said tapping her watch.

He stared at her appearing as confused as she felt.

"Oh," her father said.

She looked at him. "Oh what, Dad?"

"I turned your watch back along with all the clocks. When you were out for a jog. Just to be safe."

Her mouth fell open. She covered it. "Dad. It's a thirty-year-old game. How could you think that..."

Finn leaned forward taking the clock from the table. "You set all the clocks back. For good luck. I get it."

Her father smiled.

"You get it?" she asked. "How on earth can you possibly get it?"

"He told me all about it."

She felt as though she'd walked into an alternate universe. "What are you doing here? I mean, should I call the police? You're stalking me?"

Her father yanked open the side-table drawer and pulled his wallet out. "Brought my wallet back."

"Your wallet was lost?"

"Apparently."

She put her hand to her forehead. She was going to have to keep a closer eye on things. "You didn't know it was missing?"

Finn stood. "It's all right. It fell into safe hands with the post office and—"

"He's a ballplayer, too, Chloe."

She looked at the man in front of her. He hadn't mentioned that in his profile.

"Played at Alabama. Like me. Can you believe the luck?"

Chloe shook her head.

HighBall7 took the flowers from his bag. A few stems drooped, others bent half over. "They looked better a few hours ago."

She looked at her watch. "What time is it?"

"Nine-fifteen."

"Oh my God. I'm sorry. You must have thought..."

He handed her the flowers, nestling them into her arms. "I saw your picture on the wall when your dad invited me in and I nearly fell over and..."

She couldn't believe what she was hearing. She looked down at the flowers, the full weight of them settling in. "Ranunculus."

"It took some looking."

She petted the heads. "You must have searched all day." She thought of the humiliation her last boyfriend handed her just as easily as this man offered her a bouquet. "Thank you," she said.

"Better head out 'fore the dancehall closes down," her father said. He shook the remote at them. "Time for Matlock."

Finn and Chloe looked at one another. She felt a tickle in her belly, like the organza butterflies sewn onto her skirt fluttered inside her. She looked out the window. "But the snow. Really coming down. They'll close early."

"A walk then?" he said, eyebrows lifted.

Yes. She wanted that, but no words came out.

"I mean if you want to."

"I'll have to change my shoes."

"Okay," he said.

"Okay," her father repeated. "I can't hear Matlock with you two yammering. Put it on in my bedroom."

And so with her father tucked under his covers, watching Matlock, Chloe kissed his forehead.

Boots on, cape back over her shoulders, Finn held the door open.

She hesitated, struck by the complete sense of comfort with this stranger. *This can't be right.* She started to back up and make an excuse for why she shouldn't go.

But then he reached for her, his hand brushing the back of hers. And in a magical way she'd only read about in other people's stories, her fingers slipped into his and they headed into the night, love at first sight, as real as the snow that covered them while they walked for hours.

Back at the house, sun just about coming up, she shivered. He pulled her close, his arms tight around her, his hand pushing into her hair, lips on hers. And the world shifted, those minutes capturing first light, the first hours of new love, and the kind of luck a couple needed to start a life together, happily ever after.

LOVE ON THE EDGE

Kimberly Kurth Gray

Mrs. Parker had been a widow for twenty-nine years and was quite practiced in proper etiquette for her status. She kept her clothes modest, wore only a touch of lipstick on special occasions, and never invited a member of the opposite sex into her home.

The red Austin Allegro in front of number 29 did not go unnoticed by Mrs. Parker. Tilly Adams lived there and had recently become a widow herself. A tall man with dark hair left the house as she watched.

Tilly waved as he drove off, rather too fast in Mrs. Parker's opinion. When the red car was out of sight, Tilly made her way across the street.

"Having your dinner delivered this evening?" asked Mrs. Parker as Tilly came to stand near the gate.

"You mean that man? No, he's someone I met this afternoon. He returned my wallet that I stupidly left on the counter at the coffee shop."

"Tilly dear, you must be careful. What would the neighbors say if they'd seen a man at your house?"

"I'll keep that in mind," Tilly said.

Mrs. Parker especially had been fond of Jason, and often said he was like a son to her. But it wasn't motherly feelings that drew the other neighborhood women out in their lawn chairs to watch him mow the grass. His blond hair and athletic build garnered a fan club everywhere he went.

"I know it's lonely, but you'll adjust and you have me right here whenever you need a chat," Mrs. Parker said. "We widows need to stick together."

Mrs. Parker's words replayed as Tilly lay in her bed that night. Forty-eight seemed young to be a widow. Was this the rest of her life, eating and sleeping alone and chatting with neighbors for entertainment? She threw the covers off and stared at the ceiling.

It was true she'd met Daniel at the coffee shop, but he wasn't over because she'd left her wallet. He came because she'd invited him. While Tilly had been deciding her order, Daniel began to place his own order, thinking she was done. He apologized profusely, insisting he'd pay for her coffee. That was two weeks ago. They'd met for dinner twice since and once went to a movie. Daniel had let her choose the film. Tilly wasn't accustomed to being asked her opinion.

When the Allegro showed up the next evening, Mrs. Parker ventured closer to the fence to hack away at the hydrangeas. The front of Tilly's house was dark, but she could see light spilling out from the kitchen door casting shadows across the driveway.

Kayla Campbell came out from next door and stretched, readying herself for an evening run. "You're going to have nothing but stumps if you keep at it," she said and leaned over the fence.

Mrs. Parker looked down at the purple blossoms now strewn along the sidewalk. "I guess my mind was elsewhere," she said turning to Kayla. "Do you know who owns that car?" The older woman pointed across the street with her hedge clippers.

"Nope. Is it a friend of Tilly's?"

"I'm afraid she's gotten herself into a situation she's unable to handle," said Mrs. Parker. "We may need to help her."

Kayla hadn't been in Mrs. Parker's kitchen since the afternoon Jason Adams dropped dead on his front lawn from an aneurysm. They sat around the large Formica table, each of them in an avocado green laminated chair. How had she ended up here again?

Mrs. Parker wasted no time gathering the women who lived nearest to her. She'd tempted them with baked goods and gossip, both things they all denied enjoying, but nevertheless partook in all the same.

"She must still be in shock," said Octavia Jenkins. "I mean, really, who expects a young, healthy man to die? He wasn't even shoveling, just blowing snow around."

"I won't let Clay buy one. They're bad for the environment." Amma Jones rocked her infant as she spoke. Jemma had been born the night Jason died though Mrs. Parker knew she'd considered naming the child after her neighbor in remembrance if it had been a boy. Clay would've pitched a fit. He wasn't as enamored with Jason as his wife and the other women who lived on Edge Drive.

"This is the second night he's visited. Who knows what's on his mind." Mrs. Parker sliced banana bread and pushed it toward the women. It was nice to have company in the kitchen again.

"Maybe they're going on a date," said Octavia. "No one would expect her to stay alone for the rest of her life."

"But it's not even been six months since Jason passed," said Mrs. Parker.

"Four months and seventeen days," Amma said.

Each woman nodded with a glazed expression as they remembered that December afternoon. Jason's golden blond hair glittering on the snow in the sun. They missed his tanned face and muscular body, his white even teeth, his clear light blue eyes that warmed when he smiled. They all sighed. Embarrassed, each woman grabbed something and quickly made themselves busy with food and drink.

The next evening Daniel had to park his car a block away. "Hello, love," he said when Tilly answered the door. "A neighborhood party? Have we been invited?" He smiled down at her, his eyes, nearly the color of navy blue, sparkled.

Tilly leaned out the door and was astonished to see all her neighbors' cars parked at the curbs and their driveways empty. "No party that I'm aware of," she said and led him into the house. They'd barely sat down when the doorbell chimed.

"Hello," said Octavia. "I made way too much spinach lasagna and remembered how much you and Jason liked it, so I brought you some." She squeezed around Tilly and made her way into the living room. "You have company."

"Yes, we were..." Tilly began.

"There's plenty. Let me get the plates." Octavia went into the kitchen and began pulling dishes and cutlery from the cabinets. "You sit here, hon." She directed Daniel who obediently sat at the far side of the table.

"This is my friend Daniel Berker," Tilly said as Octavia pushed her in a chair at the other end.

"Pleased to meet you. I'm Octavia. Tilly and me been neighbors since she and Jason moved here to Edge Drive." She slapped a square of lasagna on Daniel's plate. "Eat up. You look like you could use a good meal." She sat between them and helped herself to a portion.

For three hours they ate, talked, and drank the wine Daniel had brought. Octavia was rather tipsy and needed to be escorted home. "You be good to our Tilly," she said as Daniel bid her goodnight.

"I'm sorry about that," Tilly said when he came back.

"Why are you sorry?"

"Because your plans for a quiet evening were spoiled."

"My plans were to spend time with you and I've done that," Daniel said.

Tilly's face flushed and her throat was dry, probably from the wine, but as Daniel approached her she imagined it might be something more.

21

Kayla rose early the next morning to go for a run. She noticed the red Allegro as she snapped her dogs into their leashes.

"I believe he's stayed the night," Mrs. Parker whispered through the shrubs. "What in the world is she thinking? This type of relationship won't fill the void a husband leaves." Not that Mrs. Parker was absolutely sure of this. There'd been no one since her Arthur had died in 1991.

"Octavia's lasagna must not have been bad enough to send him packing," Kayla smiled.

"It's not funny," said Mrs. Parker. "Something like this could tarnish Tilly's reputation if word got around."

Tilly was over forty years old, thought Kayla, and well beyond worrying about her reputation. Other than Mrs. Parker, who really cared about the men their neighbor dated? She had to admit this guy seemed an unusual choice for someone like Tilly. She was the kind of woman who grew herbs and sent Christmas cards. The man who drove the Allegro was more of a guy you'd meet in a club, all smooth moves and empty promises. Kayla couldn't imagine Tilly in a bar.

The dogs pulled at their leashes as Kayla and Mrs. Parker stood watching number 29. Much to the younger woman's horror and the older woman's seeming delight, the front door opened and out stepped the man. Though she wanted to turn away, Kayla watched as he kissed Tilly full on the lips then bustled down the front steps giving her and Mrs. Parker a salute and a wink.

"Time to implement plan B," said Mrs. Parker.

Tilly shut the door without acknowledging her neighbors. She'd expected Mrs. Parker to keep her under surveillance, but not Kayla. Surely her younger neighbor wouldn't be judgmental of having an overnight guest. Tilly's cheeks warmed at the thought of Daniel sprawled across her bed. Her knees began to shake so hard she had to sit down.

Daniel had made coffee and brought her a cup as she lay in bed. In all the years she had been married to Jason, he'd not once brought her coffee, though he would have for any of their neighbors. Appearances had been extremely important to him and he lapped up the adoration from the neighborhood women.

He'd been a good husband, hadn't drank to excess, worked every day, and took exemplary care of their house and property, but he'd never shown the same care toward Tilly. It was as if he didn't need to worry once they were married, and instead of tending to their relationship, he wooed their neighbors.

Tilly wandered from room to room tracing her fingers along the furniture that had belonged to Jason's grandmother, the walls painted white the way Jason liked, Jason's trophies he'd won playing tennis and lacrosse.

She began to make a list.

"A bridge club? You serious?" Octavia asked between bites of peach cobbler.

"We need to give her something to do, something appropriate for a widow," answered Mrs. Parker.

Octavia chewed the cobbler until it became mush in her mouth, fearing the words that might escape her. She'd been reprimanded by the old woman twice already for not only failing her mission, but now it was somehow her fault Daniel had spent the night.

She didn't have the nerve to tell Mrs. Parker that she thought Daniel was a nice man, that he'd been polite and kind, and handsome in a disheveled way. Of course his British accent and compliments of her cooking didn't hurt her opinion of him either.

"We don't even know how to play bridge, and what makes you think Tilly'd want to play with us anyhow?" Octavia finally said.

"I'm not sure I understand why there's so much opposition to Tilly's friend," said Amma. She lusted after the cobbler, but since she had to lay across the bed to snap her pants, only tea passed her lips. "Octavia said he's pleasant enough, and Tilly's happy."

"Happy?" Mrs. Parker scrunched up her nose. "She doesn't know what she's doing. She's still in shock over losing Jason. This man's obviously taking advantage of her vulnerability."

Amma sat back against her chair and patted Jemma's butt trying to ease a burp from the baby. They now knew the man's name was Daniel. He was attractive, maybe around fifty years old with striking blue eyes. Amma imagined he might be rather fun in... well, she shouldn't think about that.

These past weeks, though, it was all she could think about. Clay hadn't been interested in nighttime activities since the baby. Last night she'd seen Tilly and Daniel through the window. Her breath caught as she watched him take Tilly in his arms. Amma had run upstairs and changed into an alluring nightgown only to discover Clay asleep next to Jemma's crib. She'd crept back to the window facing Tilly's kitchen, worried she was turning into Mrs. Parker.

"What about a book club? I know Tilly likes to read." Mrs. Parker's voice brought Amma back to the present.

"We could read romances," Amma suggested.

"No, absolutely not. We don't want to encourage her. We want to keep her mind busy. I say we read a biography."

"Julia Child," said Octavia.

"Marilyn Monroe?" Amma asked.

"Gloria Steinem," Kayla said and pushed her plate away.

Mrs. Parker shook her head. These women were going to be no help at all.

Tilly answered the door with a paint roller in one hand and streaks of green across her cheek. "Hello. Is everything alright?"

"I thought I might have a word," said Mrs. Parker. She walked into the house though she hadn't been invited and put her hand to her mouth when she saw the room. "What have you done?"

"Like it? It's called Zen Green. I thought I'd freshen the place up."

"Tilly," Mrs. Parker said. "I can see you really need me."

"Do you mind if I continue painting while we talk? I'd like to get this room done before dinner."

"I'd rather you not." Mrs. Parker lifted a corner of the tarp Tilly had covering the sofa and sat. Tilly kneeled on the floor. "I'm worried about you, dear. It's not been a year since our Jason has passed and you seem to be letting your grief cloud the decisions you're making. First, meeting a man and now..." Mrs. Parker waved her hand around the room.

"I'm only painting. Jason usually does this every three or four years," Tilly said.

"Touching up the color is one thing, but this is completely different. You may hate it tomorrow."

"I may," Tilly conceded, "but I can always paint over it."

"True, but you can't paint over a mistake you make with a man. Tilly, what if this man..."

"Daniel?"

"What if this Daniel thinks you mean to have a serious relationship with him? He may be searching for a wife, and what if he moves in and you realize it was only loneliness that led you to this lapse in judgment? You won't be able to rid yourself of him easily."

"Mrs. Parker, I barely know Daniel. I'm not thinking of marrying anyone or having a roommate. I'm just tired of white walls."

"You say that now, but I've seen the way he admires you. This would be a comfortable spot for him. He's smooth... Octavia said so. Remember who you are, dear. You are Mrs. Jason Adams and you must honor your husband's memory."

It took Tilly an hour and three beers to wash away the taste of anger she had swallowed with Mrs. Parker's words. "A book club!" shouted Tilly and threw her bottle in the recycling bin. She stood in the middle of the living room and stared at her unfinished paint job. She'd lived in this house for fifteen years and there wasn't one trace of her in any piece of furniture, lamp or decoration. Even the kitchen towels had been purchased by Jason online.

Loneliness hadn't come to Tilly in her widowhood, it shadowed her since the day she'd married Jason. The accusations Mrs. Parker said had made her upset, but also made her think. Was she rushing into things she'd regret?

"How are you?" Daniel called across the street to Mrs. Parker who was sweeping the curb. She turned back toward her house pretending she hadn't heard him. He was now parking in the driveway even though the neighbors had abandoned her plan and were no longer parking on the street. With the red Allegro nose to nose with Tilly's car, everyone could plainly see what was happening. Three weeks had passed since her chat with Tilly, and all her warnings had been disregarded. This Daniel person was there more often than not. She caught glimpses of Tilly in the yard or at the door. Mrs. Parker ignored her when she waved in the same way Tilly had ignored her friendly advice.

"Come on then," Daniel said as Tilly lingered at the door. "She's a bit of a mad cow and her mood will blow over in time."

"She won't look at me," Tilly said. "I baked her favorite chocolate cake, invited her for tea. She wouldn't even return my call."

"Why do you care so much?" asked Daniel. "Your other neighbors give the impression of being nice and mostly normal. Bake them a cake, invite them to tea."

"I don't need their..." Tilly waved her words away. "Nothing. I'm being silly."

Daniel put his hands on Tilly's shoulders and had her face the mirror above the mantle. "See her? This is the only person whose approval you need."

Tilly smiled, but closed her eyes and hung her head. Daniel turned her toward him. "Open your eyes," he said, gently lifting her chin and rubbing his thumb across her lip. "You don't need approval from anyone, not Mrs. Parker, or Octavia or any of the others, or even me. You should do what you want."

Tilly had known for the first time what she wanted the day she'd met Daniel.

"Will you help me?" she asked.

"I will do whatever you tell me to do," he answered.

Tilly packed in boxes every last part of who she was as Mrs. Jason Adams and lugged them to the garage. She'd put ads in the paper for the furniture and sold many pieces. Hopefully the rest would sell at the community yard sale. She painted the other rooms while Daniel planted wildflowers and vegetables so there was no longer a lawn to keep up.

Mrs. Parker stared from her porch, but still refused to acknowledge greetings. The rancher seemed more like a home than it had ever been. Tilly liked the green walls and she liked Daniel. There would be no turning back or regrets.

"Would you look at that?" Octavia said to Amma. "Mrs. Parker has done pruned her hedges to death. They are so threadbare, she's got nowhere to hide anymore."

"Why won't she come over?" asked Amma. "Tilly's selling some nice things. We've got baked goods and hot dogs and it's a beautiful day. Is she mad with all of us?"

"We've failed to rid Tilly of Daniel," Kayla said. "And yes, I believe she's upset with everyone. I couldn't even set my table up in front of my own house because she kept squirting it with her hose."

Octavia laughed. "She's going to be awfully lonely over there."

"She already is. Don't you get it? Jason's dying created a bond for her with Tilly. They're both widows. She wanted them to be companions."

"I'd never thought of that," said Octavia. "But that doesn't make it right for her to be angry at Tilly... or us."

Daniel stood quietly listening to the women as Tilly grabbed change from the cigar box for her latest customer. The older widow hid in her living room behind the curtains. He saw her each time they fluttered.

Mrs. Parker hesitantly answered the door. She knew her caller; she'd watched him cross the street.

"Good afternoon, Mrs. Parker. I don't think we've been properly introduced. I'm Daniel Berker. Tilly tells me you make the best peach cobbler on the block. In fact, she believes it's the best in the state. Tilly's made one herself today and she thinks it might be a bit heavy on the cinnamon. I'm no expert, you see. I say it's delicious, but I think maybe you should test it."

Mrs. Parker was determined to say no. He had a lot of nerve knocking on her door, but he really was much more handsome close up. Not in the same way as Jason, of course, but those deep blue eyes and that charming accent made it hard for her to ignore him. "Tilly's a fine cook. I'm sure her cobbler is good."

Daniel held out his arm. Mrs. Parker glimpsed back into her empty house before linking her arm through his. The women watched as he led the old widow to them.

"That's a nice car you have," Mrs. Parker said. "My husband was fond of cars."

"Is that so?" asked Daniel, giving a sly wink to Tilly.

"You must always park it in the driveway so no one damages it." Mrs. Parker pressed her lips together. She only wore lipstick on special occasions.

A MINUTE–LONG LOVE

Hilary Hauck

The real part of our love story lasted for one single, glorious minute out of the four hours we knew each other. As for the rest, well, that was between me and the stars.

The minute happened on Labor Day weekend 1941, when folks still talked about staying out of the war.

I didn't think she'd noticed me at all. I couldn't compete with Huey's rendition of "When You Wish Upon a Star" from the top of the Ferris wheel, or the way Anthony won a goldfish for every girl in the group, even if he had thrown enough ping pong balls to fill three swimming pools.

Gerry had been the one to pull the evening together. It was us boys from school and a group of girls, one his cousin from Spangler. We joked the whole walk to the fair. They bet Gerry would get to first base, Anthony would get the prettiest girl, Huey the plainest. I didn't mind that they forgot to bet on me.

I noticed her right away. Shy, rosy cheeks, barely looking at us guys but giggling with the braver girls who didn't think twice about linking arms with one of my buddies.

If you asked a friend, they might tell you how I, too, tended to hang back a bit, which is probably why it took until the roller coaster, the last ride of the night, before I sat next to her. She screamed when we went over the first hump, but I didn't have the guts to hold her hand until the last descent. I was as happy as a dog with two tails when she didn't pull away.

Gerry's uncle was waiting at the bottom of the roller coaster to fetch the gals. I bet he'd turned up ten minutes early on purpose, knowing that given the chance, we guys would be trying to seal our goodbyes with a kiss.

It's not much of a love story. I didn't even get to say "so long," but it was all I had. One single night, a single ride holding hands. A moment a luckier guy might have forgotten, but it was enough to get me through a war.

Things may or may not have been different if the darn world as we knew it hadn't changed. The war that belonged to other nations had become ours—the Japanese gave us little choice. So instead of heading to learn a trade as I'd intended, there I found myself in an olive drab jacket and leather cap toe boots on a train heading for boot camp.

None of us knew for sure what awaited. The best we could conjecture was that we'd soon head overseas, off to fight an enemy from some other part of the world who we'd never have a quarrel with if it weren't for this blasted war.

We placed our bets on Europe. Who could be sure? But what we did know was that the train was going by Hastings, which wasn't too far from Spangler, and that's where she was. Only this was a no stopping train and I had no way of knowing her address. Heck, I didn't even know her last name. All I knew was that her first name was

Eleanor, she was sixteen, and had flaxen curls and wore a blue dress with white flowers on it.

Leaning on the edge of the train door's window, I watched the countryside for signs we were getting close, past restless swells of hills, farms dotted between woodlands. Most of the time a creek meandered by the side of the train. Not that she had any reason to be at the station, but you can't blame a guy for dreaming. Then in the nick of time an idea occurred to me. It was a shot, a really remote one, but it was better than nothing.

I scrambled in my mess bag for the pad of paper and pen Ma had given to me, telling me for the hundredth time to write.

> *My dear Eleanor, I don't know if you remember me, we held hands on the roller coaster. It's crazy really, we barely met, but I've thought of you every day since. I'm off to war, but it'd be mighty swell if you'd consider waiting for me. I'd like to walk out with you, maybe catch a movie or dance—do you like a good waltz? As you have no way of answering, I'm gonna take the liberty to think of you as my gal until I get back. Until then, my darling. Walter. (Gerry's tall and lanky friend)*

I folded the paper then wrote on the outside of it: Please deliver to Eleanor, aged 16, Spangler. I couldn't just hand a piece of paper out of the window to a stranger and hope they'd deliver it, so I took a shiny quarter out of my pocket and wrapped that in another piece of paper.

On it I wrote: *To whomever delivers my letter to Eleanor, for your trouble.*

I leaned back out of the train window. I could see the buildings of Hastings up ahead. Even if we didn't stop, we slowed down through towns, and there'd be someone to toss my letter to. But, taking me unawares, just a coupla hundred feet from the station, a voice called my name. I pulled myself back in the carriage to find Mr. Jones, a banker close to my father's age.

He asked about the family, the usual niceties, then his voice dropped an octave as he asked about my deployment. The town sign came and went past the window behind him. I kept talking, sharing what little information I knew about going to war, in part because manners dictated, but in part because it'd occurred to me that he might find a way to get the letter to Eleanor for me.

We must've gone a hundred feet out of the station before the corner of the note tickled my palm, as though reminding me of its mission. "Mr. Jones," I blurted. "Can I ask you to deliver a letter for me when you get back home? If you'd be so kind, sir."

"'Fraid not, son. I won't be going back. We are relocating to the city of Altoona." He pulled himself straighter and tugged his jacket lapels. "I have been invited to manage a city branch of the bank, you see. Worked my way up since—"

I never did hear when he'd started to work his way up. Might not have been my proudest moment, but I turned my back on him and stuck my head back out the window as fast as you could say gobbledygook.

It was no use, I'd missed it. The station was drifting away behind us, my hopes of getting the letter to Eleanor with it.

I put the note back in my pocket. At least I'd saved the quarter since money was hard to come by. I went to sit back down, but the thought stung me as bad as those hornets that one time at Grandpa's barn. What would the chances be of ever meeting a gal who could flip my heart like that? I woulda given a thousand quarters to see her again.

We'd just passed a dairy farm. Now the land was opening up to a field of potatoes. Without a second's more thought, I threw the letter, aiming for the little bit of land at the edge of the field that's kept clear. My chances slung in a row of dirt between ditch and crop.

I stood for a time at that window, looking back long after the field of potatoes had slipped from view. A lot of stars had to align for that letter to get to her, but those stars were all I had.

The war does things to you, things you don't want to talk about. To have seen what you've seen hurts in a way nobody should ever hurt. And those days I felt as lousy as lousy could be. First I was terrified of dying, then relieved I didn't die, then guilty as hell that I didn't die when my buddies did.

At first you think you'll remember every damned day, as well as each of the days we didn't fight or march, the kind of days that you'd expect from a bunch of young men at a summer camp. But even those days dragged on, until the whole affair became a green and brown mishmash of bland mush on a tin plate, blistered feet, and the moans of men suffering, physical like, or at night, hurting just from the horror of it.

Whenever our regiment got letters, you'll think me ridiculous no doubt, but I always held out hope there'd be one from her. Catching me up on news back home, gushing details about how she missed me, what we'd do when I'd get home safely. The paper she wrote on would be perfumed, colored pink, pretty as her.

I'd always feel a pang of regret when I shuffled through the letters from Ma and my sister and occasionally a cousin from Maine, then settle in with my back against the canvas of my pack, pretending I'd chosen to read those first, savoring the anticipation of her letter for last. When I was done reading, I'd clasp my hands on my belly, close my eyes and dream of what she'd have written, if only she'd known how to find me, and I guess that's how the love story blossomed in my head and became something real.

You could just say that love story saved me. In the bleakest times of war when I'd started to believe I'd dreamed the days of Ma's macaronis, my little sister's singing to her dolls, of picking up the eggs at Grandpa's barn, when a sinking feeling'd set in that life would never be anything but war again—in those dismal moments, I'd notice the stars. Not look for them exactly, but wake up in the night and the clouds would part just so, or a buddy would look up and you'd follow his gaze and he'd just happen to be looking at the stars. I'd think of Eleanor, and I'd want to live another day.

There's no rhyme or reason to which man lives through a war and which doesn't, no reason for why I was still standing when the war ended and most others weren't. We cheered on the outside, but I don't think a single one of my buddies could ever feel real glee again in their lives. Not the kind of glee that sets in your gut until sundown. But still, we acted jolly for a few days. A tough mood to keep up even when you're so near to going home.

It wasn't just us, there were men all over the world to gather up and ship back home. The hanging around and the short stints of moving onto the next stage of our trip chafed at our patience, but then one day we made it onto a ship and it was as though that waiting time hadn't been long at all. Each day we sailed, all that pain and exhaustion started to slip away from our memories just as Ma's cooking and details had felt like not-quite reality during wartime.

Every night on that ship I sat on the deck and watched the stars. You'd think I'd be about to tell you how I was getting more and more excited about going to see Eleanor. I wish that was how this next part of the story went, but truth be told, each night the love fell away from those stars a little bit more, mile by nautical mile, mocking me, if a star could mock. The love story had existed in my head and now my heart would be held to account.

There was little hope she'd even got the letter, even less that she'd waited nigh on four years for some kid with spots who'd held her hand for a single minute. By the time I reached home, I'd settled myself onto the idea that my story with Eleanor was over.

I slept a lot that first week. When I did get out of bed it felt like I was still dreaming—the feasts Ma prepared, of mac and cheese, haluski, real bread, all on a china plate. Then I made a point of visiting my buddies' families, those of them I needed to tell about their son's last days. Gerry's Pa and Ma were the hardest. I told them all what a good fella their son was, as if it'd help there pain any.

I needed to learn a trade, figure out the rest of my life, but the only time I could focus without the sounds in my head of men moaning or the vision of Gerry's blistered feet the day before he got blown up was when I was visiting someone, and their pain seemed to outdo mine. But I'd visited all the family I knew I had, and all the families of my buddies, and the thought kept nagging at me that the only person I had left to call upon was Eleanor.

I might never have done it. I might have let the story stay just a story I told myself to get through the war, but one day, life seemed to be telling me to call on her.

It started out that I found a quarter by the road, glinting in the mud. I didn't pick it up, I left it for someone who needed it more than I did. The point is that it got me thinking of the quarter I'd thrown to the edge of the field. Next thing I know, some guy at the old company store was talking about Spangler when I stopped to pick up flour and lard for Ma. If that weren't two signs in a day, that night after supper Gerry's ma stopped by with a pie she'd made for me, seeing as it was Gerry's favorite pie and she couldn't make it for him anymore. Of all the things, she'd cut out pastry stars and baked them on the top.

So that was what sealed it. What made me go looking for her, even if it was only to face the fact that our love story had all been in my head. She'd surely never got the letter. Only the stars could have told her about our story.

I gave myself all sorts of talking to, that she'd been sure to have married some other guy, one she'd probably known her entire life, and I'd tell her how happy I was for her. She might even be a mother with younguns like my sister, Audrey, who didn't seem like she was anything more than a bitty girl herself. But restless as these thoughts made me, the fear of being alone with my memories weighed more heavily than the thought of finding her with another love.

It was a sunny day in May when I borrowed a car from Huey's dad. Chilly, the trees were still trying to put out new leaves and it crossed my mind that it'd been winter here the whole time, that maybe the countryside had paused while we were off fighting, but of course it hadn't— it just felt that way.

Sure, I didn't know where she lived, but small towns are small towns, right? Even this one that liked to call itself the longest little town in the world. Everyone knew everyone. The very first person I saw was a boy, probably all of twelve. For that I was grateful—a grown-up would be more likely to judge when I made a complete fool of myself.

"Hey kid," I called. "Do you know a gal called Eleanor? Flaxen hair, in her twenties now?"

"Sure do," he said, and I could see his eyes feasting on the car. "What about her?"

"Will you take me to her?"

The kid looked up the street, then down the street from where I'd come, then back at the car. He put his hands on his hips, like he was meaning business. "I'll show you where she lives if you let me ride in the car."

"Hop on in, why don't ya?" I told him.

We'd barely gone two hundred yards when he gestured for me to turn up a street, and pointed to a house. "She lives there."

I stopped where he pointed. An ordinary house, like the rest of the ordinary houses on the street. All those years of feeling like ordinary life had been something I'd dreamed, the dream of regular life stood right there in brick and mortar. And inside of it, perhaps, a slim chance, my dream gal.

That thought got my stomach in a bigger knot than a ship's anchor. All these months and years, waiting for this chance and now I couldn't dare face what the outcome could be. But I had this kid in the car with me, who had touched just about every control there was in just this short stint. He was my excuse to put things off a few more moments.

"Much obliged. Wanna come for a spin before I call for her?"

Need I tell you what his answer was? We must have hit every street at least twice. Another thing about small towns, a motorized vehicle doesn't cruise around unnoticed. This time we pulled down her street from the top end, saw right away a group of people had gathered outside her house and stood on the grass.

"Who are those people?" I asked.

The kid shrugged, then he asked, "Are you the guy who wrote Eleanor the letter?"

"Bet there are lots of guys who write gals letters," I said.

"The one with the quarter?"

I stopped the car and I swear the boy's words stopped my heart. "You know about that?"

"Everyone knows. The olds talk about it all the time."

Someone had found the letter. Everyone knew about it. And from the looks of the group of people standing outside Eleanor's house, the news that I was looking for her had traveled as fast as a pierogi down a hungry man's throat.

I pulled the brake tight. I hadn't dared look directly at their faces yet. This moment suddenly mattered more than any other moment of my life.

I stepped out of the car, knew I should tell the kid not to touch the controls but I couldn't make the words come out.

I walked up the path toward the people, still not daring to look right at them, and so I saw her shoes first— how I knew they were hers, I cannot tell you, but I did. Pretty leather ones with a nice solid heel. And so when I looked up, hers was the first face out of that crowd I saw.

All the times I'd dreamed of that moment—good dreams mostly, more recently ones where she was married already, or where she didn't even remember me— nothing could have prepared me. When our eyes met, it was like we were back on the roller coaster, her eyes shimmering with excitement, only this time it wasn't because of no ride or goldfish or a song from on top of the Ferris wheel.

"Eleanor," I said.

"Walter," she said, and as though the greetings were done and over, she ran—yes ma'am, she ran toward me— right into my arms.

"You waited," I said.

"What took you so long?" she asked. Then as natural as can be, we walked into her parents' house.

That quarter, the one I'd wrapped in a note for whomever delivered it, still sits on Eleanor's bedside table. She wrapped it in a handkerchief and tucked it into her purse on our wedding day. Turns out the kid who'd found my note and delivered it hadn't felt he needed to keep it, it'd been no trouble to him to get the letter to her. But me? I woulda paid him a thousand quarters for what he'd done—and I'm sure I have. Hired him as soon as I'd finished learning how to repair clocks and taught him the craft. We opened a clock shop nigh on forty years ago.

Every night I close up shop, go home for supper, then I go and check on the chickens Eleanor has been keeping ever since our children grew up and moved on. I look up at the stars, spare a thought for Gerry and the others, and I thank the stars for my gal.

NOTE: This fictional story was inspired by a true story as told to the author by Maribeth Shaffer.

FOR CHEEKU

Madhu Bazaz Wangu

A new sun rises, golden yellow, exquisite.
You spread freshness of swaddled joy in my lap.
Lips velvety petals, black amber eyes, silken eyelashes.
Fussy cheeks, wrinkly neck, dimpled hands.
Delight rises from the bottom of my belly, my heart, my head.
I am showered with bliss.

"Do you know who I am?" I ask, smiling from ear to ear.
You simply stare.
I can't stop hugging, can't stop kissing until
you lay in your bassinet under moonbeams.
When you cry, adoring parents wrap you in a cocoon.
You lull back into a womb like trance.
Kisses on your forehead, on your cheeks, on your tummy
leave a sweetness in me lingering like a lullaby.
My cradle song puts me to sleep to treasure the day in
my dreams.

Two years pass like butterfly flits.

You smile back when I kiss cheeks no longer fuzzy.
I kiss your chubby hands and plump fingers, tiny toes
and little soles.

Belly kisses make you giggle.
Your kisses sweet, your hugs gentle, your smiles like
buttercup blossoms.

My heart overflows; I burst into tears.
Nani's life is fading like the red and purple farewell of a sunset.
I taste innocence and tenderness.
I savor the joy of your smiles, kisses, and hugs, my Cheeku.
I watch life sprout and blossom to perfection.
I see miracles happen; I live.

WHEN TO DROP THE L-BOMB

James Robinson, Jr.

When it comes to matters of love, a friend once advised, "My mother always told me you shouldn't love anything that can't love you back."

How apropos indeed.

Having survived the '60s version of love, I've come to the conclusion that many have forgotten its true meaning. They have lost their way, gone off the rails, missed the target, thrown a few too many darts against the saloon wall, or, as the modern generation might say, swiped right too many times. What with high divorce rates, online dating, breaking up by email, and coping with the infamous breakup line, "It's not you, it's me," no wonder love is confusing.

But I'm not talking about its romantic, emotional aspects. Most of us know what it's like to love and receive love from another warm body, all head over heels with the magic, swooning at chick flicks (not me), or rooting for or against the Bachelor and Bachelorette du jour. My concern is that we're fuzzy on terminology. We need clarity. We need a road map, a clear-cut guide to when and how to use the word appropriately. We need a Love GPS— *In 300 feet, make a U-turn and don't use the "L" word again.*

It disturbs me when I see so many confused souls casting the term about willy-nilly, as if it were some kind of emotional frisbee. Friends and relatives use it to escape uncomfortable phone calls. After a brief conversation they hurriedly say, "Okay, love ya, bye."

It's a cheap tactic, a ruse tantamount to breaking up via text. I toss a symbolic yellow flag—Personal foul: misuse of the "L" word.

Sure, they love their better half, but in this case, the act is disingenuous. This ploy wouldn't work with my wife. Like an attorney looking for legal precedent, she knows I've never laid the groundwork for such amorous proclamations. I'm just not the type to end a call with, "I love you." My son-in-law and my oldest daughter do it, but with them, it's a tradition. And it's done with sincerity. I don't even like talking on the phone, so you're lucky if you get a goodbye.

Come to think of it, I'm not all that big on talking face-to-face either.

Maybe I'm jealous. I was born into an Oscar the Grouch family. No one was big on hugging. I am still not a proponent of kissing hello or goodbye for no reason. The only good reason might be a kiss before non-elective surgery or returning from a life-or-death stay at a Vietnamese prison camp. Maybe.

But I also don't gasp and throw out the "L" bomb every time I get turned on by some inanimate object, when a "Wow, that oriental lamp is really dope," would suffice.

The biggest embezzlement of the "L" word is the master manipulators—the kings and queens of the home facelift. Ladies and gentlemen of the jury, may I point the long, gnarled index finger of guilt at the fixer-upper shows. Why place the blame squarely at the feet of home makeover perps? Because they lead innocent homeowners down the path to the "love it" junction—a place from which they can never return. A place where viewers become entangled in mushy refrains, in search of their (cough) forever homes, all the while giggling like teenagers taking selfies before the prom.

Lookin' for love in all the wrong places? "Oh, I love the wood floors." "I love the vaulted ceilings." "I love the deck." "I love the white cabinets." "I love the open concept. It's (gulp) great for entertaining." People who love open concepts always love to entertain. And then there's: "I love what you did with that peninsula."

Peninsula? An interesting term. I always imagined a peninsula in a kitchen as a misplaced land mass surrounded by bar stools.

Listen, there's not enough love in the world. Especially for inert objects. Then Christianity makes an appearance. "Oh, my God. Oh... my... God. I can't believe this. It doesn't look like the same house." Wasn't that the idea behind remodeling, Rosie?

It happens at concerts, too. I've heard those choruses of passion hurled from crowd to stage. Teenage girls—admiring fans of boy bands—yell sweeping adorations to their favorite idol. "I love you, Robbie," they scream with tears streaming. The band member might even return her proclamation. "I love you, too," they hasten to say. Unfortunately, they probably made the same decree to a different fervent fan in Cleveland the night before.

Fifty years later, my wife and I still joke about admiring Peter Cetera fans at a Chicago concert yelling: "We love you, Peter!" when he was still with the group way back in the early '70s. Cetera was apparently over and done with that type of adulation because he continued to play bass and declined their exuberance.

Peter left the group for a solo career. I'm not sure if his admirers followed.

Yet I must make one confession. Nearly a decade ago, after writing and directing a church play, I gave a heartfelt speech to the audience and proclaimed to the cast: "I love you all!" Yes, I was overcome at the time. I knew the cast well and was good friends with most of them. And, yes, they fit the they-could-love-me-back requirement. But I didn't really love any of them. I merely appreciated their hard work. I was proud of them for what they did in bringing my work to life. It was an emotional gaff. I didn't love them in the true sense of the word. Come to think of it, the male lead in the play, though talented, was a real pain in my butt. I chucked an "L" bomb at that cretin and I didn't even like him.

Another offender is men talking about their vehicles. Repeat after me, guys: "I like that new car." "I am in awe of the soft leather seats and the sunroof." But you can't love an inanimate object no matter how hot it is. You might fantasize about that new C8 2020 mid-engine Corvette all you want, or its ability to go from 0-60 MPH in under 3.0 seconds, or the fact that it's being compared to Ferraris. You can even say it's a chick magnet. Hey, I could see one in my garage. I would kick my boring, utilitarian SUV out into the cold, cruel driveway.

But don't say you love it. A shiny sports car won't love you back. That 3,500-pound heat-seeking missile won't keep you warm on a cold winter night. Even a cold-hearted woman can throw off a little fire.

You also shouldn't love your man-cave, guys. It's just a place where you retreat to get away from the world and hang out, maybe have a couple of brewskies with the fellas. But could you really have the same caring feelings for that vaulted ceiling as you do for that precious, blonde, six-year-old daddy's girl? I didn't think so.

And last, but certainly not least, this proclamation makes me shiver, longing to take a hot poker to the eye of the offender. "I love my job." Try these more suitable alternatives: "I enjoy what I do," "I look forward to going to work," or "My job is rewarding." But you don't love your job. I guarantee it. Not only can a job not love you back, but it will only pay you for your love in cash. You can pay a woman on the street to do that. Sorry.

So just remember, love is a strong affection, a kinship, whether spoken or unspoken to another individual. Love your sis, love your mom, love your bro, and your favorite Uncle Bill. I'm sure you have a special place in your heart for good ol' Grandpa Joe—that is unless he's one of those perverted old men you have to keep the kids away from during family cookouts.

As the Doobie Brothers once said, "Listen to the music." It's all about love: *I Will Always Love You*; *Love is a Many Splendored Thing*; *What the World Needs Now is Love, Sweet Love*; *All You Need is Love*; *Can't Help Falling in Love With You*. Music is about life and love and broken hearts. We're talking about loving one another, here.

Don't waste one single "L" bomb on a Louis Vuitton bag. Love songs don't lie. Even Country-Western ditties.

As for me, I know from whence my love comes and goes. I love my wife and adult children. I also love my six grandchildren, although such love is filed in a different place. I would swear the two youngest have "666" etched somewhere on their little bodies.

I cherished all of my children and grandchildren the first time I saw them. They were instantly a part of me, and as soon as they were old enough, I could sense the love flowing in both directions. I love my parents because they unselfishly raised me to be the man I've become. Such as I am.

Animals hold their own link on the love chain. While I've had a deep fondness for many pets in my life, I've never called it love, although some others do. Those dogs and cats became members of the family, but I felt a different kind of affection—something between fondness and attachment. Their feelings never wavered. Whatever they felt, it was constant. I shed many a tear when they died but I never knew quite where to put the loss—not equal to losing a human being, but a strong bond, to be sure. Who knows what their feeling was for me? Perhaps an animal's version of devotion.

Whenever you use the word "love," employ the "Will the recipient love me back?" test. Or better yet: "Would I give my life for the object of my affection?" While I would give my life for my close family—my wife, those kids and those special grandkids—I can't say the same for anything I bought, sold, or acquired. Think before you drop the bomb, people.

Don't let those sappy homeowners on the "Lucky Humpty Dumpty Network" (knock down a wall and put it together again) lead you astray. No stainless-steel appliance or granite countertop is worthy of the almighty "L" bomb.

I love you all.*

*Oops!

JUST GIVE IT SEVEN DAYS

Amy Morley

Sophia opened her mouth to speak, but instead, shredded lettuce projected across her car dashboard, followed by a guttural belch.

"Uhh? Are you okay? Are you in a wind tunnel? Are you driving?" Duane's voice sounded from the speaker phone function of Sophia's BlackBerry KeyOne. She strained to hear him over the wind as she coasted down Route 173 toward home.

"No, no, yes, both, I don't know," Sophia said. "I'm sorry. Hold on."

She pulled her Nissan Sentra into the parking lot of Forta Industrial and had mere seconds to shift into park before she felt the burn rupture her esophagus again. Barely making it out of the driver's seat, she stumbled onto the pavement, just in the nick of time. Her body lurched forward.

"Is that water splashing? Where are you?" she heard Duane's voice through her phone. "Sophia, why did you call me?"

And that was when it finally hit her, much like the bad lettuce, along with the pseudo-date she'd just abandoned with a different man whose name she couldn't even remember. She didn't ponder the fact because it proved insignificant, a symbolic ending of her evening... uncontrollable projectile vomiting. Tonight's date had felt much like the asphalt she was standing on—artificial, imitation, fake.

As Sophia's guts screamed in pain, she was glad her instincts had told her to call Duane, a man she met a few weeks prior through mutual friends, and subsequently kept her mind occupied when she was with someone else. Until that moment she hadn't realized the feelings she had for him. In a time of fight or flight, of the thirty-seven contacts in her phone, Sophia made the snap decision to call Duane Mook-Clayre.

"Sophia, I'm still here. What do you need?" His voice echoed through the speaker.

"What do I need?" Sophia leaned against her car for support, standing over a puddle of her own puke in the abandoned parking lot. In that moment she realized she needed Duane Mook-Clayre.

Sophia pushed the end call button, crawled back into her car, and drove the remaining five minutes down the street until she reached her home.

It had been a few weeks since Duane had last heard from Sophia. When they met, it was infatuation at first sight. But she was out of his league for sure. The best he could ever hope for was her friendship. She wasn't like other girls he had dated. In fact, she wasn't like any girl he had ever met.

Duane found her interesting, and intriguing, even more so now, after their last conversation mid-vomit. Yet

Duane wasn't put off by it. He hoped to see her at the summer luau-themed party thrown by their mutual friend Jessica. He peeked around the back of the house. He thought he saw Sophia's red Nissan turn into the driveway. Moving closer he saw a clearer image of Sophia sitting in her car as she checked her hair in the rearview mirror. He watched as she messed with it for a moment then rolled her eyes at herself, got out of the car, and began walking toward the front door.

Duane moved to the iPad dock and switched the Pandora station from Pop Coast Hits to Hawaiian Reggae, then continued out to the deck, and up the stairs through the sliding glass door into the house.

Sophia turned off the ignition and checked her hair in the rearview mirror one last time. She was still contemplating if bangs were a good look on her. Shrugging, she knew there was nothing she could do about it now. She got out of the car and walked up the cobblestone path toward the front door.

With a mini cactus plant in hand, she peered through the screen door, then entered. She heard muffled voices, and the echo of some steel-drum type music radiating assumingly from Pandora, as after the song an ad for Tide sounded out. Walking further toward the back of the house, Sophia placed the cactus on a hallway table. Staring at the plant, she realized it was quite pitiful, not at all a good hostess gift for a summer party she'd reluctantly agreed to attend.

She knew she would see Duane, and hadn't gotten over the embarrassment of the last time they spoke—when she called him, for no other reason, than to have him witness the joyous sounds of her deep into an episode of food-poisoning.

Sophia heard the sliding glass door open. Then, a voice. It was Duane's. "Perfect," she mumbled under her breath as her memory drudged up every embarrassing detail from vomit-gate.

"What are you doing up here all alone? Come join the party," he said as she turned to face him.

"I just got here. I was making my way down back," she said as her eyes darted toward her shoes. Of all the people to be alone in a room with, it had to be him.

"Hang on a sec." He ducked into the bathroom.

Sophia paced back and forth the thirty seconds he was in there. It gave her time to move that pitiful cactus next to the fruit bowl on the kitchen island so nobody would know its gift-giving origins. She placed it next to the overripe bananas, which hid it partially.

"Look at that pathetic thing. Sheesh. Jess really should put it out of its misery," Duane said as he walked into the kitchen. Sophia made eye contact. His smile put her at ease.

Whew. "Right? A cactus?" Sophia said. "When did Jess begin getting home décor tips from the Southwest? Is she channeling D'Angelo Vickers or something?"

"Nice reference!" Duane raised his hand to give Sophia a high-five. "I didn't know you were a fan of *The Office.*"

"I didn't think anyone would get that," Sophia said.

"Are you kidding? It's the greatest show of all time."

"I think you meant to say that *Seinfeld* is the greatest show of all time," Sophia chided.

"Never saw it," Duane said.

"What? Well, you need to change that," Sophia said. "The entire series is on Hulu."

"I'm more of a Netflix kind of guy."

"Get out!" Sophia gave him a slight Elaine Benes-style shove.

"Whoa, whoa, whoa, what was that for?" Duane laughed and jokingly backed away from her at the same time.

"You would know if you'd ever watched *Seinfeld.*"

"I just might check it out then. Thanks for the recommendation." Duane looked down at her and smiled.

Sophia continued, "I have Hulu. And Netflix. And Prime. And Dog TV. So, if you ever need ideas on what to watch, say no more." She cocked her head to the side as she looked up at him and smiled back, her cheeks turning slightly red.

"Dog TV it is then," he said still smiling, then their eyes locked. Duane rubbed his hands together and shifted from one foot to the other.

Sophia stood there in silence waiting for what would happen next. Ever since she had met him, their conversations were so easy, but at times like this he left her speechless.

"I guess I could get a free seven-day Hulu trial," he suggested.

"Well, yeah, there's that." Sophia's eyes darted back down to her shoes. Then, awkward silence continued for what felt like an eternity. *That was my moment and I blew it. I had the perfect opportunity to invite him over. Why didn't I take it?*

Duane thought about asking her out, but she'd only just arrived at the party. If she wasn't interested in him, he didn't want to make her feel obligated to say yes—or worse, decline—and then they'd both have to spend the night dodging each other.

Duane had come to realize that as easy as it was to talk to Sophia, once she relaxed she tended to pull back. He needed to figure out a way to get her to open up. He wanted to know why she had called him the other night.

"I'm going to go back to the party." Duane slid the sliding glass door open. He turned slightly but continued, "Oh, uh, one more thing, Sophia. There's potato salad on the buffet that's been sitting out for a while. I just don't want you to throw up again. Not a good sound on you at all." He then slid the door closed and walked toward the music.

Sophia felt her jaw drop and froze. She was too confused, and slightly humiliated, to hang around any longer, so she turned on her heel and went out the front door.

"So, you aren't coming then?" Duane spoke into his iPhone X. His brother Theo was supposed to be meeting him to see the seven o'clock movie. "Well, I already bought the tickets so it's too late. No, don't worry about it, your daughter is running a fever, I understand. Tell Daniella that Uncle Duane hopes she feels better."

As if on cue, just as he hung up, he saw Sophia Saponaro turning the corner and walking toward him.

"Are you here to see *Sack Lunch*?" she asked.

"What?" Duane replied with a confused look.

"*Prognosis Negative*?"

"Uhh..."

"You haven't watched *Seinfeld* yet have you?

"Yes, I have."

"Oh, really? If you had then you would know exactly what I was talking about. Okay, wise guy, give me another movie title. Or shall we dial Moviefone?"

"We can try but we might end up calling Kramerica Industries," Duane said.

His response apparently caught Sophia off guard. "You did watch it," she said quietly. "I didn't think you would."

"Only a few episodes..." Duane's voice trailed off.

He noticed a look of panic cross her face, then she asked, "Are you meeting someone?"

"I was supposed to," Duane said.

"Oh." Sophia was obviously displeased with his answer.

"What about you? Are you meeting someone?" he asked.

"No. Never. I always go to the movies alone."

"Why?"

"I don't know. It's just something I do. Always have."

"People actually do that?"

"Yes, people actually do that!" Sophia laughed. "And apparently you are one of those weirdos today, too, since your date canceled on you! At least when you go places alone, there's less of a chance you'll get ghosted."

Duane explained what really happened to Sophia and he thought he detected a wave of relief.

"Poor kid," Sophia sighed.

Duane realized that, once again, he had the perfect opportunity to ask her out, then he thought back to the asinine comment he'd made at the party. *I am such a tool. It's a wonder she's still speaking to me.*

"Yeah, poor kid." Duane looked away for a moment, "She'll be fine. It's me I worry about. I have never seen a movie alone before. And now I have this extra ticket. Should I try to scalp it?"

Sophia reached into her wallet. "Here's ten dollars. Get me some popcorn and a Sprite. This movie has been out for a few weeks now. It's the best offer you are going to get. Come on. I don't want to miss the previews."

Two hours later as they walked out the theater doors and onto the pavement, Sophia finished up the last sip of Sprite. "It's funny, I never thought I would actually enjoy sitting with someone at the movies." They began walking toward his Jeep when she stopped and told him she only lived down the block and needed to walk the other way.

Duane took the empty drink container from Sophia's hand and tossed it in the trash. Turning back to her he said, "It's funny how our paths keep crossing. You call me one night throwing up into the phone and since then I haven't been able to get rid of you."

Sophia was confused. Why did he keep bringing that up? "Not my finest moment, but there you go again," she said. "I panicked. Your number was the first one I saw in my phone. I don't even know why I thought calling anyone would be a good idea, let alone someone I didn't know very well."

"You trusted me," Duane said. "Can I walk you home?"

Sophia nodded and then said, "I did, didn't I? Which is so unlike me." They walked in silence for a minute before Sophia continued, "I don't trust many people. I am not really a 'people person' like you are."

"You don't say?"

Sophia noted the sarcasm. "You noticed that, huh?"

"Well, we do have the same circle of friends... and it's a small circle."

"I only just moved here a year ago, and it's a small town. Slim pickings..."

"Is that why you choose to spend all of your free time with me? Am I the best option?"

"What about you? Am I the best option? You've lived here all your life. You know so many people. And yet you end up alone at the movies on a Friday night."

"But, Sophia, you choose to be alone. Why?"

"I'm not alone now, am I?" She looked toward the porch light and pointed at it. "This one is me. I'm home. And my two dogs, Oscar and Bruce, are waiting inside. So, I am not alone."

Duane stood there and watched Sophia walk up the three steps leading to her porch. He wanted to follow, but all of a sudden he clammed up. Sophia made him feel such at ease, and yet uneasy at the same time.

"Are you just going to stand there?" she said from the porch. "Come on, let's go inside."

Following her into the split-level craftsman, Duane took in his surroundings, not noticing that she had gone into the kitchen. "Wow. This house is huge. It's like never ending rooms." He sat down on the couch in the parlor.

Sophia returned through the opened pocket doors, handed Duane a glass of iced tea, and sat down next to him. "Sorry it's not from Long Island. The only thing I ever drink is water and iced tea, and the occasional Sprite."

"You couldn't scrounge up a Bud Light? You don't keep any in stock for when you have company?" he asked as he poured several sugar packets into his glass.

"Well, no," Sophia said, but then paused. "You are the first person I have ever invited over to my house."

"You're kidding."

"No." Sophia thought about it as she sipped her iced tea. "I've lived here for a little over a year and you are the first person, other than my realtor, who has stepped foot in this house. I guess I am destined to be alone forever." She crossed her legs shifting toward Duane, inching her body closer to him, and staring intently into his eyes.

"Not me. I want to have a house full of kids. I cannot wait to propose. I can't wait to get married," Duane said, but then his expression changed, like he'd said something he regretted.

As Sophia heard those words, she felt her heart drop to her stomach. "I didn't realize you were dating anyone." She uncrossed her legs, turning slightly away.

Duane shuffled in his seat. "Actually, I don't have a girlfriend right now."

Sophia stared at Duane with a wry smile and felt herself relax once again. Moving closer to his end of the couch she asked, "How does that make sense? You can't wait to propose, you can't wait to get married, but you don't have a girlfriend?"

"I don't know how to just go out and get a girlfriend," Duane admitted.

"It's not that hard," Sophia said.

"It is too hard. It's scary," Duane confessed. "I am afraid of rejection. What if she doesn't like me back?"

Sophia tried to stifle a laugh but couldn't. "Duane, we're in our mid-thirties. You are acting as though you are in junior high school. It's easy. You meet someone you like. You ask her to hang out. Like how it happened tonight. I like you, I didn't want the night to end, so I asked you to stay."

"Sophia, you've actually become a really good friend..." Duane trailed off as he took another sip of his drink, studying the ice cubes to avoid eye contact.

"I don't want to be just friends anymore. And I don't think you do either." Sophia gulped, suddenly realizing there was no sense denying her true feelings.

"You're right," Duane replied, looking up into her eyes but then darted them back down and stared at the floor. Taking a deep breath, he continued, "But what if it doesn't work out? I want us to still be friends."

Sophia realized that they both put too much pressure on themselves. What each was hoping for was right there all along. She wondered if having no expectations was the way to go.

"Duane," she said, reaching over to hold his hand as she looked him in the eyes. "Will you be my boyfriend? If only for a week? Just give it seven days. If after seven days your life has not improved, then we can end this and go back to being just friends. I am only asking for a week."

"Is this a sales pitch?" Duane laughed.

"Just give it a week," Sophia said.

He looked at Sophia with the realization that she was the one. *I will give you a lifetime. But let's start with seven days.* He pulled Sophia in and held her close. "Okay. I'll give it seven days."

ASTARIA'S TOOTH FAIRY ADVENTURE

MaryAlice Meli

The other fairies and I waited outside Tooth Fairy School on our first day. They were jumping and laughing, but I was scared. My grandmother had been a star tooth fairy. So was my mother. What if I was too clumsy? What if I flunked tooth fairy school? I thought so hard about the what ifs, I forgot to keep moving to the school door. I felt a gentle hand on my back.

"You looked worried," said a fairy with a periwinkle blue face wearing a feathery, rainbow dress. "My name is Celeste."

"I'm Astaria," I said, "and I'm scared and super worried."

Celeste flash-closed both eyes, then opened one.

"I worry, too, but we're going to love it."

"How can I love it when it scares me?"

She smiled. "We can worry together!"

"Mom and Granny loved their tooth fairy careers. I want to love it, but I'm afraid I'm going to be too clumsy and stupid."

A fairy with a sea green face, gave a mean HAH-ha laugh. She pushed Celeste and bumped me to get to the front of the line just as we marched inside.

The school looked like a big, round, furry bubble with clouds of teeth around it. Large front teeth for biting hamburgers and apples, small side teeth for crunching cherry popsicles and bubble gum and big back molars for chewing pizza and hot dogs.

The Mean Green fairy stuck out her foot and tripped me. Everyone laughed. Commander MichaelAngela told us to sit down. They laughed again when I fell over a tooth seat and my bag of sparkles flew open.

Before dancing out the window, the sparkles floated around glossy white teeth hanging from the ceiling. Commander MichaelAngela snapped her wand at them and they flew back into my bag. She looked so fierce the string on my drawstring bag tied itself.

I was so surprised I got the hiccups, and everyone but Celeste laughed.

I was happy to have a friend at Tooth Fairy School.

Commander MichaelAngela asked the whole class which tooth falls out first and no one knew the answer. Whew! Not even Mean Green.

Commander MichaelAngela divided the class into partners and gave everyone a Twinkling Tattling Tooth Tablet. We were to wear them around our necks on buttercup yellow straps. She said we would learn about them later.

Then Captain Warhol, our supervisor, marched toward us in his tall, pink boots. "Line up and follow me to Fairy Field for inspection," he shouted, "and don't let the line wiggle."

Everyone but me was wearing the new feathery rainbow Tooth Fairy uniform. I wore my grandmother Astra's old Tooth Fairy uniform with ten different-colored fluffy skirts, each glowing and glimmering in the dark. I felt so fancy.

Mean Green and her HAH-ha-ing friends laughed at them. "You'll never fly," Mean Green said, and her friends laughed, "HAH-ha."

Celeste grabbed my hand. "Don't pay attention to them."

"You look like a fat fairy in that old uniform," Mean Green said.

"I'm not fat," I yelled back. "I'm fluffy. And I'll fly faster than you any day." My skirts fluttered so much the wind lifted me off the grass just as Captain Warhol came to inspect our group.

"Astra? Is that you?" he asked, his voice low and soft.

"No, Captain Warhol. I'm Astaria. Astra is my grandmother. She gave me her dress."

Captain Warhol smiled a bright pink smile and said, "Astra was my partner, the most famous of all tooth fairies before she retired. Astra invented the Twinkling Tattling Tooth Tablet. Whew, that's hard to say. Anyway, the TTTT is wonderful; it beeps when teeth get loose."

He frowned and his voice deepened. "You will earn the right to wear a new skirt for every lesson you master, Astaria. But for now, you may wear only one skirt. Make Astra proud." Then he turned to Mean Green and said, "Stand straight. No slouching."

Mean Green made a mad face at me, her skin a darker shade of apple green.

Today I wore only one of Granny's skirts, a flowy purple with shiny, rippled edges. Wow. I had a lot to learn to be able to wear all ten skirts.

With a sweep of his hand, Captain Warhol turned the class over to Teacher Picasso who bobbed his bald head and began our first lesson.

"Pay attention," he crackled in a scratchy voice. "The tooth that falls out first is..." He bounced up and down on his long, purple legs and kept us waiting and waiting. "...is the tooth that gets loose first, of course!" Teacher Picasso chortled so hard his goggles slipped down to the tip of his nose.

Two boys who played guitar and drums in a rock 'n' roller rink band raised their hands and asked in two-part harmony, "How will we know when a tooth gets loose?"

I shrugged my shoulders at Celeste, and she shrugged back.

Teacher Picasso told us to click the word Loose on our Twinkling Tattling Tooth Tablets.

"When a tooth becomes wobbly and swingy and achy," Teacher Picasso said, "your Twinkling Tattling Tooth Tablet will sound the Toothometer signal."

Suddenly, everyone's Twinkling Tattling Tooth Tablet made a loud, "Blaaattt."

"Like that!" Teacher Picasso said. "That's the Toothometer signal. Now, click on the icon of a tooth on your Twinkling Tattling Tooth Tablets."

We did.

The screen showed a little girl with dark brown hair in a house on Anthem Court.

The Twinkling Tattling Tooth Tablet beeped, "Uh-oh, uh-oh, uh-oh," as she sat on her bed moving one of her front teeth with her tongue. Back and forth, back and forth.

Then the Twinkling Tattling Tooth Tablet's beeping changed from, "Uh-oh. Uh-oh, Uh-oh to Oooooooh."

Teacher Picasso said, "Oooooooh means the tooth is changing from 'Uh-oh' – just loose – to 'Ooooooh' which means verrrry loose: a swallow risk. So get ready for our first pre-pull field trip," he said, "to help little Vittoria pull her tooth before it falls out. She might swallow it if it comes loose when she bites a hamburger or an apple. Follow me to the Sparkleopter for your first field trip."

The Sparkleopter, a yellow egg on green grasshopper legs, seemed small. As we bounced up one of the long legs, its body stretched wider and wider until it fit all of us inside. Teacher Picasso poured his bag of sparkles into the Sparkleopter tank beside his seat and we lifted off under a shower of red and blue and green sparkles.

Teacher Picasso guided the Sparkleopter right through the window of little Vittoria's room without scratching the glass or ruffling the lacy curtains. Vittoria stayed fast asleep with the sparkles floating over her.

A large, stuffed rabbit under her arm wore a ribbon around his neck that said, "Rocket."

"Hello," the bunny said, waggling his whiskers at us. "How many tooth fairies does it take to pull one kid's tooth?" No one laughed.

Teacher Picasso stuck his long, purple legs out of the Sparkleopter and stood on Vittoria's bed.

"Rocket, meet our new class of tooth fairy students making their first pre-pull visit."

"I was beginning to worry," Rocket wrinkled his nose. "Vittoria's been loosening her tooth by wiggling it with her tongue."

"How are we going to help pull it out?" Celeste asked. "Won't it hurt her?"

Teacher Picasso said, "It's easy." He reached inside his pocket and pulled out a Toffee Lollee, a chewy, sticky candy on a stick. Teacher Picasso gave it to Rocket.

The bunny smiled and clasped it in his paws. "I'll see she gets it." His whiskers rippled.

Next day, our second lesson was Tooth Money. Teacher Picasso gave each of us a little green bag that clinked when we shook it. "Check your Twinkling Tattling Tooth Tablet and click on Vittoria," he said.

When we did, we saw four shiny quarters on the screen.

"Vittoria is from the United States, so her money is American," Teacher Picasso said. "If Vittoria were a little girl named Li in China or Sofia in Greece or Berthe in France or Maria in Italy, the Twinkling Tattling Tooth Tablets would show a yuan or a drachma or a franc or a lira."

"But how much do we give them?" I asked.

"Check your Twinkling Tattling Tooth Tablet again," Teacher Picasso said. "Parents decide. For Vittoria, her mom and dad say she may receive $1.00."

Just as we readied to click on our Twinkling Tattling Tooth Tablets, the Toothometer blurped a "Blaaattt," followed by a wailing "Waaaahhhh."

Teacher Picasso said, "That's the third and final reading: A 'Waaaahhhh' means the tooth is out and ready to be collected. Follow me."

We climbed into his Sparkleopter and whisked back to Vittoria, snug in her bed covered by a frilly white coverlet. I loved how softly we landed.

I was worried what to do if a little boy or girl wakes up. How could I stop feeling scared?

Rocket the rabbit was smiling as we crawled out of the Sparkleopter.

"I gave her the sticky candy and her tooth came out right away," he said. "But I thought she'd never fall asleep. She was so excited about a tooth fairy visit."

"All right, class," Teacher Picasso said. "Open your money bags and take out one coin."

I clutched the smooth cool metal disc and could see the sunny tan glow from my face in its mirrored sides.

"One of you will reach under Vittoria's pillow for her tooth," said Teacher Picasso, "and leave the money in its place."

We gathered around Vittoria like fluffy, bouncing balls of sparkling, colored lights. Teacher Picasso sat on Vittoria's wooden bed post, his long, purple legs nearly touching her pillow.

"Who would like to make this first tooth collection?"

We froze. Who would be brave enough to volunteer?

A loud voice shouted, "HAH-ha, I will."

Of course, it had to be the loudest, meanest, snobbiest fairy of all. Was I a bad person to think these things about Mean Green? She bounced over Vittoria's sleeping body, dove under her pillow, and stuffed a coin in the hollow that had held the tooth.

We watched as tooth fairy magic turned the coin into a crisp, new one dollar bill. Mean Green held the tooth in her fist and bounced up and down all over the bed yelling, "Yahh, yahh, HAH-ha, I got the first tooth."

Teacher Picasso shook his head at her. Why was she so mean? Mean Green was the one who blabbed to Captain Warhol that I had scratched Teacher Picasso's Sparkleopter with my big orange shoe. It's hard to like someone like Mean Green.

Before we learned anything else, we would get our own Sparkleopters.

I thought everyone was going to get a big Sparkleopter with springy legs like Teacher Picasso's. But a real Tooth Fairy Sparkleopter fits on top of your head just like a bicycle helmet. It's easy. You dump your bag of sparkles inside the flap at the top then lift off and steer it with your arms up or down or straight out. Swooping and soaring are the most fun. Landing is the hardest. Slowing down isn't easy, either. We had a flying, soaring, swooping day. And, uh, some splatting, too.

Splatting happens every time I try to land. I need a lot of practice.

Celeste and I practiced together. We checked our Twinkling Tattling Tooth Tablets for pre-pull customers and found two—a little boy named Andy and an older girl named Evelyn. They lived in the same house because Andy and Evelyn were brother and sister. His first loose tooth was in front. Hers was a bigger loose tooth in the back. We packed two Toffee Lollees.

Celeste and I swooped past Andy's window. He was already asleep holding a teddy bear. At Evelyn's window, we saw her playing with Barbies. We decided to land in Andy's room first.

Celeste had no trouble. She was so graceful. She glided to Andy's room and passed through the glass silently, gently settling onto his race car bed.

I tried to glide but heated my sparkles too much. I swooped to Andy's window faster than I meant to and crashed through the glass, leaving a faint scratch. I landed on the floor with a big oomph. Whew. I just got too excited about flying and steering and landing.

"Hi, girls," said Teddy Bear. "Who is that hovering in the window?"

"That's Mean Green," Celeste whispered, her eyes big and round.

"Oh, no," I said and bounced up onto Andy's bed beside her. "What's Mean Green doing here? Is she following us?"

Mean Green grinned, a poison ivy green grin, and zoomed away.

"That little Mean Green is heading back to report to Teacher Picasso and Captain Warhol and maybe even Commander MichaelAngela that I scratched the window."

Teddy Bear chuckled his long and deep ho-ha-ho-ha until his belly shook so hard, he rolled over and fell off the bed. As he did, I noticed a slip of paper sticking out from Andy's pillow.

The note said, "Dear Tooth Fairy, please don't leave money when my tooth falls out. I want a dog. Love, Andy." I tucked the note into my bag. Now what should I do?

We went to the Lost Tooth Museum for an expert's advice. Granny Astra was the director there. She showed us the first teeth lost by famous people such as Abraham Lincoln, Walt Disney, Elvis Presley, Oprah Winfrey and Taylor Swift. The teeth looked the same as Vittoria's and Andy's first teeth.

While everyone admired famous lost teeth, I whispered to Granny that I needed to talk with her. She took me to her office, "What's on your mind, Astaria dear?"

"Granny, Andy wants a dog instead of money for his first lost tooth."

"Ahh. Very interesting," Granny said.

"How will I get a dog? How will a dog fit under Andy's pillow?"

Granny laughed her little granny laugh and said, "I had a case like that once."

"What did you do?"

"I talked to the little boy's stuffed giraffe. He knew everything. The family loved animals, but their apartment did not allow dogs. Do you know what Andy's parents think?"

"No, but I know who would know that answer. So, did your boy get his wish for a dog?"

Granny smiled. "His parents took him to an animal shelter every week and let him play with the cats and walk the dogs."

Teacher Picasso's loud voice called, "Time to go. All aboard the Sparkleopter."

I decided to ask Celeste to help me talk to Teddy Bear the next day.

It was not a very good afternoon. Captain Warhol made me stand in front of everyone while he told me I had to practice flying so I wouldn't scratch anything again. I looked at Mean Green who had blabbed of my crash landing at Andy's house. Her shiny celery face beamed with joy at my trouble.

Celeste and I practiced swooping and dipping, soaring and landing all day. I got better and better at landing and keeping my sparkles cool. We practiced flying slowly just to see if we could and that's when we heard someone screaming.

"Help! Help!" called a faint, scared voice.

Celeste and I flew slower and lower to find the sound. As we got closer, the sound grew louder. I saw a flash of bright, neon green. It was Mean Green. Her uniform was snagged in a nest of thorny vines. The more she struggled to break free, the more the vines pulled her into the mud.

"Stop! Lie still and quiet," I said.

Celeste and I hovered over her. Wow, now we were hovering! We smiled at each other.

"Oh, you're happy to see me so miserable, aren't you? Smiling at my trouble."

"No, dear, we're not happy that you're in trouble," Celeste said.

"We're happy that we finally learned how to hover," I explained. "Now, we'll pull you out."

"Hurry. I'm sinking fast and it's cold and muddy," Mean Green said, her voice high and shaky.

"Your uniform is so stuck, you're going to have to take it off," I said.

"What? And let everybody see my bloomers?" Mean Green's face turned an alarming ripe avocado.

"It's either show your bloomers or stay stuck in the mud." Celeste turned around so Mean Green couldn't see her smiling.

With a green groan, Mean Green squeezed out of her uniform and floated up to us. Then her uniform floated up behind her, too.

"Here," I said, pulling out my magic waistline. "Granny's skirt can cover both of us."

Mean Green hurried to climb inside the skirt with me and nodded, not exactly a thank you but better than a HAH-ha. By the time we flew back to Mean Green's room, her face was again pale green celery and she didn't say one mean thing.

That was a surprising day.

Captain Warhol made Celeste and me stand before everyone and not because we scratched anything.

"For your bravery in rescuing another student from the wild thorny patch," Captain Warhol said, smiling a large, pink smile, "you have won a sparkling silvery ribbon."

He pinned the ribbons in our hair. We were the only fairies with shiny silvery ribbons.

Captain Warhol dismissed the class to practice flying and said, "Your classmate, Mary Grace, will return once her uniform has been cleaned of mud and repaired of all the thorn holes."

Mean Green was Mary Grace?

Celeste and I decided to fly to Andy's house.

"Guess who's going to help us bring Andy a dog?"

Celeste shook with periwinkle blue giggles. "Teddy Bear!"

We eased through the glass in Andy's window. Andy was in school. We landed on his bed beside Teddy Bear.

"Hi, girls. Celeste and Astaria, right?" he asked and chuckled his ho-ha-ho-ha-ho.

"Teddy, did you read Andy's note?" I asked.

"I don't know how to read," Teddy said.

"Andy's note said he wants a dog when his tooth falls out," I said. "But the Tooth Fairy Handbook says I can only give him money."

"Andy tells me everything," Teddy said. "I know he wants a dog."

"Do his Mom and Dad like dogs?" Celeste asked.

"Will they give him a dog?" I asked.

Teddy laughed his long, low chuckle. "I know something Andy doesn't know."

"Tell us," Celeste said.

"His mom and dad read Andy's note," Teddy said. "They said caring for a dog will teach Andy to be responsible."

"Will they put the puppy under Andy's pillow?" I asked feeling worried.

Teddy laughed. "No, after Andy loses his first tooth, his parents will take him to the animal shelter to pick a dog that needs a home."

Celeste who believed in fairness said, "And when Evelyn loses her molar?"

Teddy said, "Evelyn has always wanted a parrot."

Our Twinkling Tattling Tooth Tablets went "Blaaattt."

We clicked on the Tooth button and heard, "Oooooohhh."

"Andy's tooth is getting ready to come out," I said. I pulled out the Toffee Lollees from my bag. "Teddy, make sure Andy and Evelyn get these."

Celeste and I flew to Tooth Fairy School. We saw a group of fairies laughing and pointing their fingers at one fairy who was shouting back at them. They flew into school leaving the fairy alone shaking her fists at them.

We hovered over the angry fairy who looked up at us with tears on her sage green face.

"Mean, uh I mean, Mary Grace? Is that you?"

She nodded. "My friends don't like me anymore because my skirt is full of holes. They laughed and said mean things. They're not good friends."

I checked her skirt. The torn parts had been sewn but I could still see their marks.

"Come with me," I said and we all flew to my home.

Granny had many old skirts including one that was a soothing grass green, matching Mary Grace's skin color perfectly. She tried it on and looked like her old self but without saying rude words or stretching her face into nasty looks.

"No one has ever been so nice to me," said Mary Grace. She twirled making the skirt float out around her and began to sing. Celeste sang with her in a high, clear voice and I added my lower tones.

Just then, our Twinkling Tattling Tooth Tablets sounded, "Blaaattt... Waaaahhhhh."

"Andy's tooth is out!" I said. "Let's collect it together and maybe earn another skirt."

We decided to collect teeth as a team of singing tooth fairies.

We hovered over Andy's yard while he played Frisbee with his new dog.

"How much is that doggie from the shelter," we sang as Andy hugged his dog who gave him doggie kisses.

I love being a tooth fairy. Maybe I'll always be a little scared, but my friends help me feel strong. I think I'll be okay.

ALWAYS AND FOREVER
ALL IS AS IT SHOULD BE

Judy England–McCarthy

The soul... it calls and those who listen to its breathless
murmurings are reminded.
Reminded of the true nature of things, that we are
the absolute silence.

Our world is just our playground,
a window to view the mind's eye.
We reflect the illusions that traverse within us.
There is no side to see, all is present, past and future.

Contemplation allows the shadows to take flight
The nearer the understanding,
the more we float in an ocean of space,
open to explore the secrets of existence.

Sometimes I imagine a glimpse
then I am shrouded once again.
Exhausted I sit and struggle to see,
what is already there, within my reach.

It teases me with an ease by which it eludes my grasp.
I step lightly on the edge, teetering as though I might fall,
into the absolute surrender of the unknown.
Still shadows linger, my mind won't let go...

Will the veil ever be lifted?
A chance for me to be that which I already am.
A conscious expression of existence,
not some flimsy story of myself, but life itself unfolding.

Control is a false master who would lead me to ruin.
As I struggle on my journey toward enlightenment.
That is the crux of the problem, for there is no other.
We are just love incarnate.

Always and forever, all is as it should be.

LOVE AT THE B&B

Michele Savaunah Zirkle

Samantha Maplegood tucked her best-selling author award into the desk drawer, sopped the tears from her face and called her soul sister.

"Izzy, you know what I'm going to do?" Samantha said, squinting into the morning sun. "Hunker down here and manage this bed and breakfast, polish my nails and get funky with the next hot guy who blows my skirt up. Forget Max and his bullshit. 'I'm too busy with work to make room for you in my life, Sam.' Hell, I might even buy a plant. You know, a fucking daisy or something." She wrapped her hair into a bun on top her head. "Or a fish. Something I've got to feed or water to keep alive."

"I get it, darling," Izzy said. "Anything to avoid thinking of the Toxic One."

Samantha blew her nose. "I can't even write. Deadline for my new novel idea is three weeks away and I've got nothing. Makes me sick to think of romance. Everything I do is to the beat of this story in my head. I keep hearing his voice, seeing his wicked smile. The way his eyes swallowed me whole when he asked me to marry him."

"Sounds like you're speaking what you need to be writing, girl. Isn't your writer's retreat next month? Maybe that will get your keyboard snapping."

Samantha pressed a spoon against the tea bag in her mug. "What kind of man proposes while washing the car anyway? He put more thought into what model computer to buy."

Tears fell into Samantha's coffee mug. "Iz," she said. "Come see me. I need your famous foot rub. Bad. Oh, and bring one of those special suckers. Those and a few Tia Mia's, I can forget Max ever existed."

"Will see if I can catch a flight this weekend, bump some meetings to online. Did one last week from the tub, bubbles up to my neck and Jake in undies on the deck in downward dog... oh damn, Sam. I don't mean to salt that wound."

"Not your fault you got a keeper," Samantha said. "Bring some of that salt. We can use it to cast a spell for my next man."

Samantha pinched the candle flame dancing in the crystal holder on the stove.

"I see why this place is called CandleWick Cove now," a man said, placing his patrolman hat on the counter and pouring a thermos full of coffee. "How'd you learn to do that?"

"Same as you learned to fire your weapon," Samantha replied, pointing at his gun belt. "Sleep good last night? First night in a new place I walk into walls searching for the potty."

A pearl black cat jumped on the counter and nudged the treat bag in an open cabinet.

"Charcoal!" Samantha clapped her hands.

The cabinet door slammed, narrowly missing Charcoal's head.

Samantha rolled her shawl close to her neck and smiled at the officer. "You have your weapons and I have mine," the hostess said, twirling to face a woman dressed in a long paisley skirt and red ankle boots.

"Wind about blew me toward the pearly gates," the woman said, tucking stray, gray hairs into a blonde bun.

"Officer Riley, this is my mom, Lillian. She's lived in Portsmouth for forty years. Knows the ownership chain of each building in town. You need to find a house... she's your woman. No real estate fees or license. Around here you only need a license to practice medicine and sometimes to drive."

"Make you a deal," Riley said, smiling. "Find me a house here in Portsmouth before the baby is walking and earn one get-out-of-ticket-free voucher."

"Aw!" Samantha said. "How old is he?"

Riley ran a hand over his brillo pad head. "Six months. How'd you know I have a boy?"

"Samantha's always been a good guesser," Lillian said. "Right, dear?"

"Need a woowoo license to do what I do." Samantha winked. "Riley, you have a safe day, and Mom, it's Room 3 that needs cleaned for the doctor coming tonight. Thanks for helping me out today. This is a heavenly job, but I've got to try to get some words on the page. Never thought I'd be caretaker of a B&B."

"One on the historical registry of haunted places no less," Lillian said as Riley wiggled his fingers as if playing a piano and slipped out the back door.

"Hellooo," a female shouted over the whistling tea pot.

Samantha plopped a tea bag into a mug. "In here," she said, turning to a tall lady with black curly hair held in place by a pink headband and pulling a leopard print suitcase.

Samantha darted toward the lady and hugged her, knocking her into the wall. "Izzy!"

Izzy pressed Samantha's head to her breast. "Oh, baby girl," she said. "We must get your power back. We can't let Max—"

"I'm so ready!" Samantha unwrapped from the embrace and looked into Izzy's eyes as if the Messiah had just come. "What first? I've already cleared my chakras, saged the house and did a forgiveness ceremony—could do that ceremony every day. The waves of anger—I just really believed he wanted a life with me." She fell into Izzy's waiting arms, sobbing.

Charcoal tap danced across the bookcase.

Izzy rubbed Sam's head for several minutes. "I'm here to help you get your groove back. Tea. Dandelion if you have it, darling," Izzy requested, sitting on the barstool. "And grab yours."

Samantha poured a mug full and scooted a jar of honey across the granite countertop.

Izzy squeezed honey directly onto her tongue. "Drink up."

Samantha finished off her tea and Izzy peered into her empty mug. "Looks like a griffin in here. Wings and feet. You live between two worlds."

"Twenty-two worlds somedays," Samantha laughed.

"Grasshopper and dove," Izzy said, squinting and turning the mug. "Good luck and abundance are with you, chic."

Samantha sighed. "Luck is like the tide."

"It does leave," Izzy said, "but always returns, different and transformed just like this dragonfly." Izzy pointed into the mug.

Samantha turned away from the bar and looked out the window over the sink. A cardinal stared at her from the white fence post. News was definitely coming. She just hoped it would be the spark of inspiration she needed to forge a new path to love.

As the sun set, Officer Riley popped open a beer and kicked his feet up on the Adirondack chair on the back patio. A burning incense cone inside a hanging metal sculpture cast fairy images onto the brick wall of the house. "Amazing view of the city and the river from here."

Samantha settled into a chair and waved as if drawing a shape over her small plate of salad. "Ever seen a UFO?"

Riley's beer-filled hand stopped mid-air. "You shitting me? Have you?"

Samantha pointed toward the yellowish-pink horizon. "If it's going to show itself, it's usually around now."

The backdoor creaked open and Izzy and Lillian strode out, hands full of wine and berries. They plopped the food onto the table and sat in the swing.

Riley tipped his head toward the newest guest. "Doc, I'm looking for a house to buy. Wanted to come back closer to family here in Ohio. My wife and baby are in

South Carolina. She works and needs me to find a house so she can approve it online and give her boss notice."

Doc's bald head shone under the torch light. "Women, babies and new careers make the young heart sing."

"What about you, Dr. Braxton?" Samantha asked. "You married?"

Doc rubbed his hands together as if rubbing a genie bottle for a wish. "No, the Navy was my goddess." He glanced at Riley. "You must be proud, young man. Not easy raising a family in a world where chemtrails are more prevalent than bees."

Riley and Doc clinked beer can to wine glass.

Sam passed the crackers to her mom. "Doc, this is my mom, Lillian. She's a widow."

Lillian smoothed her blouse. "My Sam. Never did hide behind my skirt tail."

Doc peered over the wire-rimmed glasses perched tight on his narrow nose. "I'm the state prison medical director," he said. "Contracted position. More drama in prisons than I saw during my assignment as a Navy ship director overseas near Egypt." He shook his head. "Sorry I set off your security alarm when I got here. Can't remember simple things, but I can recite Dickens and Yates."

Samantha swirled her hair into a knot on her head. "Might not help you get out the door quietly in the morning, but way more cool," she said. "I can clear some of that confusion from your field if you'd like. I'm an energy healer."

"I'm game." Doc motioned her over. Samantha raised her hand by his right ear and flipped her fingers across her thumbs as if playing a musical instrument.

"Interesting stories you must have," Samantha said, blowing into her hand as if it were a birthday cake full of candles. She stepped back and drew in the air again.

"Could write a book," he replied. He held his head stiffly and blinked. "Am I going to combust? Feeling fireflies in my head."

"Fire burns confusion," Samantha said. "From the moment our seed of life is planted in the womb, a book begins growing inside us." She returned Doc's bow and added, "Namaste," the Sanskrit acknowledgment of divine love. The corner of Samantha's plump mouth curled up as Charcoal wrapped around her leg. "Every man's hand writes upon time's wall."

"Excellent!" Doc said, closing his eyes as if enjoying a fine wine. He opened them and swept his finger toward Samantha. "We have a poet in our midst. A mighty fine one. I tried to get a literary agent to no avail. Rejection letters. Ouch."

Samantha smiled. "Yes, got to have fire and endurance to be a writer—or a lover."

The next afternoon, Izzy and Samantha crawled into a crossed-legged position on the ground, knees touching under the shade of a red maple tree. Izzy sprinkled salt around them clockwise while Samantha clasped her thunderbird necklace to her heart and her other over a paper heart on her lap.

"We ask for sanctity of this space," Izzy chanted. "We call our guides and ancestors into this healing circle. We call the four directions, North, the Earth..." She grabbed a scoop of tobacco from a pouch and patted it onto the ground between them. "West, the Water," she said, pouring a stream from a tiny flask.

Samantha lit a red candle. "South, the Fire," she added. "And East, the Air." She exhaled as if trying to expel all the breath from her lungs.

Both closed their eyes, a resounding, "Ohm Shanti Ohm," echoing from their mouths and through the surrounding trees.

Samantha said, "Earth beneath me, light the way. Protect my footsteps every day. From up above to down below, make known the path that I should know. Lead me to peace. My soul longs for deep release."

Izzy hoisted Samantha up by the arm and both girls walked clockwise in the circle, eyes shut and heads low.

"Knew you'd be outside," a voice called.

Both girls looked toward the house. Lillian was standing on the patio beside a stocky dark-haired man with a bandage on his forehead. His blue eyes glistened like the surface of the ocean. Samantha blinked. *Spells don't work this fast*, she thought. *I must be dreaming.*

Izzy patted her shoulder.

Samantha's eyes locked on Max. She whispered to Izzy, "I'm not going to pass out." She took a deep breath. "I'm going to face him. Head-on." She walked toward the man while Izzy and Lillian ducked inside.

"Sam," he said, motioning to the chairs. "You look amazing. As usual." He grinned and took a seat.

She ran her hand along her neck. "Thanks," she said, sitting opposite him at the table. "What happened?"

"Was robbed," Max answered. "At a rest stop in South Carolina. Some lady called 9-1-1. Thank God for her." He wrung his hands. "Two thugs. They had a gun. Hit me with it instead of shooting me."

Samantha's eyes glazed over as she watched Max's aura exploding into jagged edges.

"You okay, Sam?"

She nodded.

"I'm sorry I hurt you," he said. "I, well..." Max pulled a cigar from his pocket. "I'm not very good at relationships."

Samantha turned her head and looked at the circle she'd just left under the tree.

Max stroked the cigar. "I want to..." he said. "Damn it, Sam." He smacked the cigar onto the table. "I love you. I want to make it work."

Samantha tossed her head back, tears streaming, and ran into the house.

Lillian knocked on the bathroom door. "Sam, let me in, girlfriend."

Samantha unlocked the door, her head buried in a towel.

"Max is squirming more than a man sitting atop a hornet's nest."

"I just don't know if I can do it again," Samantha sobbed. "It's too tough. I don't know if I have it in me."

"Angel, no guarantees in life." Lillian hugged her daughter. "With love or anything else." She cupped Samantha's face with her hands. "You're miserable without him. But you know how to fix that. Either change your perception of him and give it a shot, or, if you're really ready to be happy, cut all ties and never mention his name again. He must be dead to you if you want to heal."

Samantha blew her nose and nodded. "I know. Damn him. He still here?"

Lillian handed her a wet washcloth. "He says you deserve time to process this."

"Always analyzing everything," she said, wiping the makeup splotches from her face. "I'm always the emotional one. Sometimes I wonder if he can ever let me in that fortress he's built up to protect himself."

"The vibration from singing reduced the Tower of Babel to rubble. The higher the vibration, the more intense the feelings of love that can shatter those walls. You freshen up." Lillian opened the door. "I have a casserole in for the guests. A special request from the handsome doctor."

"Delicious," Dr. Braxton said, scooping another spoonful from the dish.

Lillian licked the wine from her lip. "Thanks."

"So, Max," Izzy said. "Do tell how you got injured. Sam says you were robbed at a rest stop down in Officer Riley's neck of the woods in South Carolina."

"Crime is rampant down there," Riley said. "I've been on the live cop show three times this year." Riley looked at Max. "What happened?"

Max tipped back in his chair. "Yesterday evening I was driving back from Georgia where I'd been on business and stopped at a rest stop near Columbia. I got out of the car and the next thing I knew a young lady with a baby was standing over me asking if I was okay.

"What!" Riley exclaimed, flipping his palm toward the sky. "You've got to be kidding me!"

"Blood was stinging my eyes and my head was throbbing. The police and ambulance arrived a few minutes later. They took a report and I didn't even remember what happened. I felt so stupid."

Riley looked at the table full of open mouths and squinting eyes. "Bet the lady had red hair." Riley scrolled through his phone and displayed a picture of a red-head. "My wife, Megan."

Max leaned in, staring at the picture. "That's her! That's your wife?" He shook his head. "She saved my life." He laid his hand on Samantha's. "In more ways than one."

Samantha pressed the crease of her napkin and glanced at Izzy. Max pressed his lips against her cheek as a cool breeze wafted the smell of honeysuckle over the patio like a blanket.

"Megan told me last night that she had seen a man getting attacked" Riley said. "She usually wouldn't have stopped at a rest stop so close to home, but the dog had to do his business."

"Amazing!" Doc said. "No coincidences."

"We are all connected. Love is boundless," Izzy offered, grabbing Samantha's hand. "Let's share a prayer."

The group interlaced hands.

Izzy bowed her head. "With this circle of love, we give praise and gratitude for all our blessings—those of friendship and support. We feel the connections that we can't see, and trust in divine timing."

Samantha raised her glass as if it were a torch. "To rekindling the flame... and to surprises."

Glasses clinked. Charcoal sauntered in and a clap of thunder sent him onto Samantha's lap, tail on high alert. She rubbed her earlobe with one hand and the cat's back with the other. Charcoal's black fur seemed to shine silver.

Doc's eyes seemed to dance above the rim of his glasses. "A chameleon cat?"

"Appearances," Samantha said, "are deceiving."

"Sure are!" Riley said, wrestling his legs onto the ottoman. "I swear I wake up every morning with less hair than when I went to bed." Riley gathered his plate. "Speaking of which. Early shift tomorrow."

Izzy stacked the empty dishes. "I'll take care of this. A normal chore would help me ground right now." Riley and Izzy carried plates inside.

Doc hopped up and offered a hand to Lillian. "A stroll, my lady?"

"Delighted," Lillian answered and tiptoed around the fern.

Max scooted his seat back as the older couple rounded the house. "Sam, I know you have no reason to believe me." He held her hands as if holding a newborn. "It took me getting hit over the head to see there's more to life than work."

Samantha bit her lower lip.

Max looked at the twinkling stars. "I want a life with you. I want to make it work."

"It's not that simple," she replied.

Max helped Samantha up and wrapped his arms around her waist. "Maybe it is."

A single tear fell from Samantha's chin as Max leaned in, his lips searching hers for the sweet taste of wine. He pulled her so tightly only one silhouette fell under the watchful full moon.

Samantha nuzzled against Max's neck. "I'm glad you got hit over the head." She raised up smiling.

Max kissed her hard—until Sam came up for air.

"Get it!" Samantha screamed. "Get it! Something is down my shirt!"

Max struggled with Samantha's flailing arms and flipped something onto the table. "There," he said, pointing to a cricket chirping from atop the daisy centerpiece.

Samantha bowed to the lucky insect. "Our new song. 'Cricket Love'."

"Got an extra bed in this place tonight?" Max asked, grinning.

"Oh, I think I can make room." Samantha hoped her gaze could send Max's heart pounding. "Just don't give me reason to rub my magic ear. It will hurt more than any board."

Max laughed. "You'd just smack me with that broom of yours." Then he led Samantha inside where Izzy was loading the last glass into the dishwasher.

"Looks like a new novel is blooming," she laughed. "Love at the B&B."

The next morning Max smiled sternly over his computer at the patio table. "This teleconference," he says into the screen, "is going to be more the norm. Working from home when possible can make us all more productive. And happy," he added grinning over at

Samantha who was on the chaise lounge snuggled up to her computer, typing and breathing in the refreshing changes... hot tea to her right and a new romance novel in the works. The characters were coming to life. The writer's block was over. Maybe her heartbreak was, too.

PRECIOUS JEWEL

Demi Stevens

Vera peered out the living room window of her condo in Springhaven Retirement Village. That Janet woman was out happily hanging heart-shaped ornaments from the pegs of her six bird feeders. How dare she! Not sure if it was the hearts or the happy that annoyed her more, Vera hid behind the curtain when Janet glanced up from her work.

It had only been five weeks since Harry died. New Year's Day. What right did Janet have already looking carefree and alive? Maybe she was ready to steal someone else's husband.

Vera couldn't resist sneaking to the kitchen window where slatted blinds would give her a more anonymous view. She watched as Janet stretched with a gigantic ornament to reach the lowest branch of the willow oak out front. No luck.

Vera laughed haughtily. "It appears love isn't the only thing out of reach now, dearie."

The teapot started gurgling on its way to a boil. Vera took a step backward, but stopped in her tracks when she spied a tall, handsome man in a peacoat striding out of Janet's front door. He too wore a broad smile and called out, "Need some help there?"

Janet practically melted into his embrace before handing over the enormous red decoration. With ease, he hooked it onto the branch, scooped up her empty basket to carry back inside, then looped his free arm around her shoulder.

The teapot let out a shriek loud enough to cause them both to turn toward Vera's condo.

Stumbling backward to get out of sight, Vera's rump hit the drop-leaf table that only barely fit in her tiny kitchen. Harry had bought it for their first apartment after they were married. The fragile china teacup she'd set out chattered a reprimand, tinkling against its saucer. Vera launched herself at the stove and extinguished the burner. Rethinking her morning strategy, she pushed the teapot onto a back burner and filled her cup with bourbon instead.

"Wonder where that hussy stole this man?" Vera fumed. "I should ask around at lunch." She glanced up at the community menu calendar on the refrigerator. "Meatloaf. No gossip could be worth that."

Her eyes wandered to the red flyer her housekeeper had posted next to it with a magnet that read: *I don't like morning people. Or mornings. Or people.* It advertised the annual Valentine's Day party at the community center.

"Maybe she's just renting an escort for tonight's dance. Someone to follow her around like a little lost puppy the way my Harry did."

When Vera and Harry had first moved to Springhaven, Janet invited them over for dinner. Vera had baked her famous turtle cheesecake and Janet raved for weeks afterward. The three of them had become inseparable friends. Janet invited them along to various activities on campus and even got Vera involved in one of the volunteer groups where she'd been able to put her gifts as a retired wedding planner to active use. There was always some event in motion. In retrospect, maybe it was just Janet's ploy to get Harry to herself each afternoon.

On this most romantic of holidays, Vera's broken heart couldn't stand the thought of balloons and glitter, but she set her empty teacup in the sink and headed over to the community center to help supervise the decoration team.

A giant red banner proclaimed LOVE IS IN THE AIR. "More like anthrax," Vera muttered and stepped inside.

The caterer was setting up a three-tiered cake on a table to the left. Vera retrieved small plastic plates and utensils from the kitchen, along with a cake knife, then laid them out beside the chocolate monstrosity. Unable to help herself, she straightened the cake topper—a cupid heart pierced by a long arrow.

"Good choice," she told the caterer. "Love is pain."

Vera picked up a package of heart-shaped balloons. That's when she saw Janet and Peacoat waltz in, arm in arm. She hastened to reach the adjacent supply room where the helium tank was stored so she could sulk alone in peace.

"There you are," Janet called to her. "I have someone I want you to meet."

Vera pasted a fake smile and extended a cautious left hand to Peacoat. Instead of a rough handshake, the gentleman cupped her fingertips and leaned forward to press a warm kiss to the back of her hand. "I've heard so much about you," he said in a sexy deep voice.

"Funny, I've heard nothing about you." Vera's skin tingled. She had been about to flail some hateful comment about adultery, but his hazel-eyed gaze kept her words in check. It was as if her heart stopped beating, and yet had only just come to life. Suddenly she felt self-conscious about still wearing her wedding ring. She clutched at the bag of latex balloons in her right hand, struggling for something more appropriate to say.

"This is my brother Mason," Janet announced. "He's come to look at buying a cottage here at Springhaven."

Vera's head reeled. So this was the mysterious brother, supposedly a banker who had never married, instead opting to travel the world on a catamaran in retirement. An hour before, Vera had been filled with jealousy. Now all she craved was to feel this stranger's lips on her hand again. To feel... well... anything.

"I... I'm..." She drew her hand back slowly from his, then straightened the hem of her blouse, grateful she'd taken the time to put on lipstick. "It's nice to meet you."

"Janet tells me there's a dance this evening. Can I help with the decorations?"

Vera admired his height, and the cut of his trousers, the way they fell neatly atop polished leather oxfords. She couldn't help but compare him to the other male volunteers in the room clad in sweatpants and orthopedic footwear.

"Oh, there's probably enough hot air in here to fill these balloons already," she mused.

His throaty laugh took Vera by surprise. "Many hands make light work," he said. "Perhaps when we're finished, you might be willing to give me a little tour around Springhaven. I'd prefer an insider's perspective, rather than some elevator pitch from the sales team."

"I'm sure your sister would be more than happy to..." Vera had been so caught up staring at him that she hadn't even noticed Janet sneak away. Her traitorous neighbor was already heading out the door, never one to lift so much as a finger to help.

When she glanced back at Mason, his head was tilted and little dimples pressed both cheeks, causing her to want to reach out and caress the stranger's face.

"I really shouldn't," she heard the words escape her lips.

"That's too bad," Mason said, his smile collapsing. "It's a perfect day for a stroll."

She'd been meaning she shouldn't touch this man's face in such an intimate gesture. Vera really needed to curb the habit of talking out loud to herself, but now her heart was racing like those Formula One cars Harry used to rave about.

She hesitantly made her way to the supply room, intermittently glancing behind to see that Mason was following. He seemed genuine in his desire to be helpful. If she were honest, Vera was school-girl giddy at the idea of working together in such close quarters.

Mason reached across her chest and expertly twisted a nozzle on the helium tank, then fumbled to retrieve a balloon from the bag in her hand.

"Oh," Vera quivered. "Why don't I fill, and you can tie? I bet you're good with those hands." She regretted the word choice as soon as it left her lips.

A wry grin spread across Mason's face. "Well, I'll try to rise to the challenge, but I might need your help."

Their eyes met and Vera's breath caught. He had moved in closer and she could now feel the heat radiating from his skin. Surprised by the power of her own body's response, she fumbled with filling the first balloon, then watched as he looped it closed in two deft motions and tied on a length of ribbon.

Fifteen minutes later, Vera was securing three balloons in a group at one of the tables in the main room and placed party favors at each place setting, while Mason appeared to scrutinize her motions. But instead of voicing some complaint or criticism, or shirking off like she'd expected, he simply took three more balloons and fastened them on the next table in a replica of her pattern, then did likewise with the party favors. Vera was astounded by his attention to detail. Why was he being so nice to her for no apparent reason?

After every table was decorated, in record time, she felt a certain sense of reciprocity toward this new man. Even her former husband had never been much good at following directions. Unless it was something Janet wanted him to do.

"I suppose we could take that tour now," Vera suggested. "That is, if you're still interested in buying a place at Springhaven." *Please be interested. In more than just a cottage!*

"I'm beginning to see its merits," Mason said slyly. "Perhaps we could take in lunch together as well?"

And dinner. And breakfast! Vera giggled, then mentally reprimanded herself. She'd only just met the man. "Definitely not," she finally said.

Mason raised an eyebrow.

"I mean," Vera backpedaled, "it's meatloaf on the menu today, and I wouldn't wish that on..." She paused, looking for just the right turn of phrase. "I wouldn't wish that on your sister's dog."

"Doesn't the phrase usually end with 'on my worst enemy'? Besides, Janet doesn't even have a dog."

An image of Harry trailing helplessly after Janet flashed unbidden. Vera waved a hand through the air and said, "There's a nice little pub in town, where they don't frown on cocktails at lunch." *Great first impression—day drinking.* What verbal diarrhea would spew out of her mouth next?

"Sounds perfect," Mason said, and motioned for Vera to lead the way.

When she and Harry had first moved to Springhaven just a year earlier, she'd hoped to revitalize their stale marriage. But after six months of unsuccessfully trying to reclaim his attention, she instead threw herself into volunteering, joining numerous committees, even becoming an usher at the symphony in exchange for free admission to concerts.

Visiting the pub had been the one activity she could always count on Harry to relish. Otherwise he'd beg off saying, "Janet invited me for an afternoon of bird watching," or "I promised I'd fix the leaky faucet in Janet's master bath." That was back when Vera still trusted Janet implicitly. In fact, she'd believed their neighbor to be a lesbian, after conversations when Janet confessed stories of a long-lost "partner" who'd died tragically.

Mason opened Vera's driver's side door for her so they could head to the restaurant, then scooted around to hop in. Such a gentleman!

Vera fumbled with the key in the ignition. "I'm surprised you wouldn't rather spend the day with your sister. She's probably still in mourning and could use the company." *What the hell? He's going to think I'm a shrew.*

"Mourning?" he questioned. "But I thought it was your husband who died a couple months ago. Condolences, by the way."

"I've felt alone a lot longer than that," Vera blurted, instantly regretting the impression she must be making on this attractive man.

Just a mile later she slid the car into a parking space outside the restaurant and slammed the brakes a little too abruptly.

"It was Janet he really loved," she mumbled. "Couldn't pry him away from your sister's side. Or well..."

It was turning into a whole day of regrets. Mason had been nothing but the perfect gentleman, yet here she was airing dirty laundry like a Tide commercial. In fact she flinched when Mason came around to open her door again before she'd even managed to turn off the engine. Why was she sharing all of this with a perfect stranger? *And I haven't even started drinking yet.* Then she remembered the teapot incident and the 9:00 A.M. bourbon, and her cheeks flushed an embarrassing crimson.

"Um..." Mason sighed. "I'm sure there must be some misunderstanding."

"Listen," Vera said, hoping for damage control. "You can hardly be held responsible for Janet's improprieties. I'm sure you've had your own fair share while galivanting around on that catamaran of yours."

"So you have heard about me," he chuckled in that deep throaty voice again.

They made their way inside and Vera was relieved when he ordered Scotch neat and didn't flinch at her Blanton's request. After they were served, he raised a glass in toast. "To improprieties..." he offered.

She clinked his glass and downed her drink in one quick motion, imagining what kind of improprieties he might have in mind.

"I'm sorry about earlier," she said. "You seem like a nice person, and it would absolutely be my pleasure to have you living nearby." Her face flushed again. *My pleasure?* She seriously needed to rein in her own tongue. "I mean, it would be wonderful to have you as a neighbor. It's just that I trusted your sister. I thought she was my friend. Until Harry started begging off to spend time with her every afternoon. And then when he was diagnosed with pancreatic cancer, he spent every evening there, too... right up until it got so bad that—"

"Vera," Mason said softly. "I think you've gotten the wrong idea."

It figured. The first man who'd expressed even a modicum of interest in her in two decades, and she'd read a future into those dimples and body heat, when Harry had only been in the grave a few short weeks.

"Oh." Vera's lips tightened into a thin line.

Mason reached across the table and placed his hand on top of hers. "I'm sure your husband loved you very much."

"Pff," she scoffed. "He had a fine way of showing it."

Their sandwiches arrived and Vera turned the conversation to Mason's stories about the boating life. Hopefully she could redeem whatever damage her sullen mood had done earlier, then as promised, she took him on a driving tour of the Springhaven campus.

Afterward, Vera pulled into her driveway and Mason sprang out of the passenger seat to come around and open the car door for her. Again.

"Wait here," he said. "There's something I need to show you." Then he loped across the street on those long lean legs and opened the door of Janet's house with a spare key she must've given him.

Vera crossed her arms over her chest and slouched back against the car door. A wash of emotions passed over her, the likes of which she hadn't felt since the hormones of pregnancy some forty years before. She'd seen their two children at the funeral, of course, and they'd stayed on to help with things around the house until the middle of January, but then she'd pushed them away just like Harry had done to her.

The sound of a garage door opening across the street jarred Vera out of her funk. She looked up to see Mason wheeling a dolly with some sort of tall cabinet on top. Janet trailed behind, looking contrite.

"Can you open your front door," Mason asked, "so I can carry this inside?"

"What?" Confused, Vera tried only to do as requested. She nearly shut the door before Janet could follow them in, then decided it was up to her to be the better person.

"Follow me to the master bedroom," Janet told her brother, and now strode confidently through Vera's small home.

Of course the hussy knows where my bedroom is. Vera's anger was about to boil over until she saw Janet help Mason unload the most exquisitely carved standing jewelry box and position it in the space she'd been saving for just such an item. In the span of five seconds all the air rushed out of her lungs. She remembered showing something similar to Harry on the internet when they'd first moved in. But he couldn't be bothered to pay attention. Or had he?

Janet lovingly ran a polishing cloth over the item while Mason wheeled the dolly out. Vera heard him open the front door. The clatter of wheels on pavement told her he must've headed back across the street to his sister's garage.

After too many silent moments, Vera opened her mouth to say something, but before she could get out the words, Janet tugged one of the drawers and pulled out an envelope. With a reverent touch, she closed the drawer and polished the handle again before turning to Vera.

"This is for you," she said.

Vera looked down at the pink envelope with her name scrawled on the front in Harry's inimitable handwriting.

She looked into Janet's eyes and saw tears escaping down the other woman's cheek.

"I... I don't understand," Vera said, taking the envelope.

"Apparently not," Janet replied. "Mason just told me you thought I was screwing your husband."

Vera couldn't stop her jaw from hanging wide open. For months she'd been harboring a wicked combination of jealousy and bitterness, though she wasn't sure whether she had been more angry about losing her husband or Janet's budding friendship.

"I suppose I can see how it happened," Janet continued. "But Harry wanted this to be a surprise. So he worked day and night in my garage, hoping to finish it before..." Her words trailed off, and now the tears began to fall in earnest.

Vera took a tentative step toward the jewelry box. It was about eighteen inches wide and just as deep, standing four feet tall. Each of the five drawers at the bottom had burnished brass pulls with heart shapes carved into the wood. On top, pulling the single doorknob on the side caused a sort of door on hinges to swing open, revealing a cedar cabinet with hooks for hanging her many necklaces. On the back of the door was a mirror, and at the bottom was a velvet-lined tray.

Cautiously, Vera set down the unopened envelope and pulled out the tray, revealing a small box with a deep purple ribbon. She turned back to see Janet now seated on the edge of the bed watching her every move.

"Harry wanted to do something special for you for Valentine's Day," Janet said. "He set up shop in my garage, but then when he got sick... he... well, he couldn't finish. He made me promise to recruit Mason to finish installing the drawer pulls and hooks... and then, of course, to deliver it to you. He said he explained everything in the card."

Vera yanked the ribbon off the box, suddenly overwhelmed with shame and grief. Inside was an anniversary wedding band adorned with inset diamonds, like one she'd once told Harry about after a client's vow renewal ceremony.

She delicately removed the ring and tried it on. A perfect fit, melding above her own wedding band and engagement ring as if they'd been designed that way.

Vera felt her world giving way, and she collapsed dizzy onto the floor.

Janet knelt beside her, rubbing her shoulder soothingly. "I can't believe I didn't see it." Then she giggled. "Guess that explains why you stopped coming over. I thought maybe... well, after I told you about my... my *partner*... that you were just an old-fashioned prude."

Vera looked up into Janet's eyes, her own now swimming with tears. "No. No!" A tsunami of emotion swelled inside her. "I can't believe I made such an awful mistake. I... I never..."

"It's okay," Janet laughed. "I get it now."

"But I... I've been so horrible to you. How can I—"

"You need time," Janet interrupted. Then she pulled back and stood. "Well... whatever it is you need, just call. But definitely join me and Mason for the dance tonight. You have to come! I think we could all use a little companionship on Valentine's Day."

After a day of regrettable tongue wagging and discoveries, Vera could no longer maintain the rigid control she'd been clinging to for months. She watched as Janet backed out of the bedroom door then turned to head home. In slow motion, Vera got onto her knees and reached inside the jewelry cabinet to retrieve the pink envelope.

My darling Vera,

I'm not much for words, but then you always said actions were stronger. Hopefully you'll look back at all our years together and remember the good times. At least now you'll have something to remember me by. You were the most precious jewel of my life.

I love you, Harry

"Oh, you ridiculous man," Vera bawled. "And me a ridiculous woman! I knew you weren't the kind to make overt gestures. Why couldn't you just pay attention to me?"

Another wave of anguish swept her as she looked down at the new diamond band, then up at the beautifully carved jewelry cabinet, and realized Harry truly had been paying attention. Just not in the ways she'd expected.

She clutched the card to her chest and felt remorse for all the terrible things she must've said during those final weeks of his life. Why hadn't he confessed what he'd been up to? Would she have believed him? Would she even have listened after feeling ignored for years before retirement?

Vera stood and looked again at the jewelry cabinet, noticing details around the mirror on the swinging door. Her reflection looked different. Still the same features, but perhaps she was now seeing a hint of the woman her husband had known. Finally allowing herself to be vulnerable, Vera dropped the façade and stared into the face of a stranger.

She placed the card back in its envelope and tucked it in the drawer. She closed the mirrored door and admired the hand-carved intricacies. She imagined Harry designing the cabinet from scratch, taking his time to assess her collection of necklaces and bracelets and earrings, figuring out exactly how many hooks and shelves and drawers would be required. She mused over how much time he must have spent picking out just the right wood, and measuring and sawing the components. He'd matched the stain of the exterior perfectly to their bedroom set, and the etchings coordinated impeccably with those on the headboard and dressers.

Vera moved to the bed they'd shared for years, reaching down to touch his pillow.

"I'm sorry I never noticed, Harry," she whispered. "I miss you. I've missed you. I hope you are at peace now."

She folded down the covers and climbed into his side of the bed, hugging his pillow to her body and resting her cheek against the cool sheets. She would survive. He obviously would have wanted her to be happy.

"Well... it's obvious to me now," she murmured, snuggling deeper under the covers like they'd done together when they first moved in at the condo, relishing the early days of retirement.

After an hour, Vera looked at the clock. There was just enough time to gather ingredients and mix up her famous turtle cheesecake to take across the street as a peace offering before the evening festivities. Vera had a lot of explaining to do, but she was hopeful her friend Janet would forgive her.

And who knows? Maybe in a few weeks or months she could begin to forgive herself. That is, if she could find a way to stop saying whatever popped into her head when gorgeous Mason was around!

ANGELICA
(A TOXIC BOTANICAL ROMANCE)

Lorraine Donohue Bonzelet

Angelica's veins oozed of envy and spite. The sap coursed around her, bleeding down to her last veinlet. The unwanted jealousy was uncontrollable – and it was all Rosemary's fault!

Before Rosemary's herbaceous arrival, Edelweiss hovered over Angelica, showering her with loving dew-drops in the morning and glistening winks of his filaments at sunset. He hung high overhead from the rock wall's crag, anchoring his roots deep into the gritty crevices.

Angelica lived amongst the wildflowers in the field below. She was grateful that she stood a solid foot above the others and closest to Edelweiss's reach. He was her Noble White Matterhorn and she was his Chartreuse Elixir.

Angelica swooned remembering the days when she would splay her umbels wide and flash her snowy starburst to get Edelweiss's attention. She wished that his silvery-white leaves would reach down to protect her from the sun and his hairy bracts caress her. Now, looking lovingly up at Edelweiss, all she could see was Rosemary's orangish underside.

A tender perennial, Rosemary sat in her terracotta throne with the other potted plants: happy-go-lucky pansies, delicately drooping fuchsia, and sweet alyssum. Her handcrafted earthenware accentuated the oversized wrought iron stand that was strategically placed against the rock wall – blocking Angelica's view of Edelweiss. The entitled plants luxuriated in a three-tiered towering complex, soaking up the organic tilth. From dawn of day until dark of night Rosemary flaunted her soft summer-blue flowers and petite sapid needles. She could almost, but not quite, touch Edelweiss. He shortened the gap, stretching his fuzzy filaments in her direction.

Angelica, on the other hand, was down with the dirt-trodden muck, disrespectfully grouped with the weeds. Her blistering sap was bubbling over! She could not allow Rosemary to connect with her true love. Born and bred on the wild side, Angelica had strong invasive and irritating qualities. But even with all of that going for her, she couldn't tackle this devious task alone. Angelica called upon the queen of poisons, Aconite. Together they would formulate a lethal toxin to take out Rosemary and win back the undivided attention of Edelweiss. Aconite, the root of all evil, was devilishly up for an herbicidal attack.

Meanwhile, the unsuspecting Rosemary enjoyed being pruned and pampered and praised. When sheared, her sprig would waft a piney aroma, an overwhelming odor in Angelica's opinion. Rosemary was the chef's top herb for exquisite meals that titillated the taste buds. Her medicinal oils were hailed for promoting hair growth, of which Edelweiss needed none. His lush wooly locks flourished just fine without Rosemary. Angelica couldn't help but be bitter! Rosemary didn't notice. She sprang upward, baring her blossoms to Edelweiss, who hung down increasingly closer to touch them.

Angelica and Aconite were running out of time. The botanical romance was growing. The deadly duo completed the toxin with a wallop of wolfbane's magic. It was sure to eradicate that fragrant foliage forever! Angelica swayed with giddiness that Edelweiss would be her true love once again.

July's Thunder Moon appeared darker than usual. Rosemary had a front row seat watching Edelweiss glisten across the rock wall like stars falling from the sky. With Aconite's addition of a flying ointment, Angelica released her fireworks. The herbicide zapped the moonstruck belladonna. Rosemary shriveled beneath the botanical stars... pulling away from her lover.

The potion was powerful. Angelica was certain of that. But she was startled as lightning bolts blazed and ferocious winds whirled! Edelweiss had awakened his ancestor's alpine whoop-ass to save the love of his life. Water gushed from the sky. Impervious to the wicked winds, Edelweiss held on steady and strong, raining his magical antidote, *salvia rosmarinus à la leontopodium nivale,* on Rosemary's decaying needles. She bathed in the moisture, absorbing his healing serum.

As the rain subsided and the morning sun rose high in the hydrangea-blue sky, Edelweiss and Rosemary intertwined. His roots stretched to their limits as her needles nestled between his comforting bracts. They would flourish together in everlasting love.

Below, Angelica was drowning with problems. Her roots were saturated. She attempted to ward off root rot while wishing away a looming fungal attack. That's when she spotted him amongst the other flowers in the new planter.

The rough and rugged cedar barrel planter was pressed against her stems. She liked that! The fresh spicy aroma aroused her. She observed the Asteraceae standing erect, in a solid six-pack, flamboyantly soaking up the sun. He was a prominent heirloom... a fire-red Mexican Zinnia in full bloom.

Angelica puffed her pleasant perfume hoping to stimulate his stamen. She got a bit sappy as she flirted, splaying her umbels.

Forget-me-not, Edelweiss, forget-me-not, but I think I'm in love with another!

My Beloved

Jennifer D. Diamond

M y Beloved,

You are the string, a loosely tossed thread, which connects me to my youth. You are the origin, the inception of my earliest childhood memories.

At two years old, my little red shoes scuffed against the flaking yellow-painted steel of your bridge. In our zero-stoplight town, it was the only avenue west. Rubber tires ripped across the open steel grates, rattling my teeth, adding vibrato to my humming as we walked high above you. I clutched my mother's hand in both of mine, convinced we would slip under the rusty railing.

Sunny summer days created checkered shadows on your swirling surface. Your rushing currents turned coffee with cream after upstream thunderstorms. Petrified of your power, I once watched as you threatened to rip our connection to the outside world off its thick stone pillars. Even as a preschooler, my parents taught me to respect your dangerous beauty.

You were then when I was little, what you are now, the true meaning of your name, "beautiful stream," the mighty Allegheny River.

You weave through my breaths when I sit still—up and down, up and down—the same as you weave through the rising and falling hills in the land where I grew up. You stitch my past to my present because even now, though I no longer live on your banks, you are with me.

When insomnia strikes, I settle my racing thoughts by conjuring your calmest waters. Scenes from my past, a time before I had any real worries, replay in my mind. Reliving those glorious moments of nothing to do all day but sunbathe provides respite from life's difficulties.

In this dreamscape, your water runs clear, sparkling with green algae, an iridescent glitter. Soothing sunrays warm my bones. Speed boats roar close, a rumble churning up your earthy smell, like an expensive organic clay facial. The dock lulls me until its wooden planks sizzle my skin with radiating heat.

Goosebumps pop when I slide my toasty body into your cool, slow-moving water. On my back, with my hair floating all around my head, I watch haloed clouds pass through the clearest blue sky. The riffles tickle me in bubbling eddies frothing around immense rocks. I marvel at how your ancient boulders were deposited as glacial debris millennia ago.

Every molecule in my body vibrates in tune with the sound of bees buzzing between mountain laurel blossoms and the wild rhododendron. To my right, a Wood Thrush sings in bright rising notes. From your opposite bank, a haunting tone answers with finality. My submerged ears should muffle these ethereal voices, but beneath your surface lies echoing clarity. Learning the language takes eons, though; not until your silty soil and gravel cover me will I truly understand.

Thirsty trees dangling from your steep banks offer cool emerald shade, a welcomed darkness. Like saturated fallen branches, my limbs grow heavy. I close my eyes. I breathe in the honeysuckle air, and my belly pushes up. I breathe out, releasing sweet nourishment for a multitude of leaves, and my body sinks. Your gentle current tugs at my middle, beckoning me to let go. Daydreams slip into sleeping-dreams.

My ever-expanding roots grow outward from you. The roots of my childhood reach through you, beneath your depths, to your twin river aquifer, purified by porous bedrock, the tap of my youth. When restless, diving into you helps me recall my most vivid memories, mining them for pure inspiration. It's not simply because I spent so much time with you that I remember you so often. It's because of you my entire life unfolded.

Hundreds of millions of years ago, before you were formed, on the land through which you now snake, a vast delta nourished the Earth. These swampy wetlands created the life-blood my grandfathers needed to put food on the table. One grandfather sat up high, his drag-line digging out coal, stripping the land open. My father's father carved out chunks of limestone until the caves were hollowed and converted into cold storage warehouses for secret government documents. After the mines were emptied, Grandpa then clocked in at the petroleum refinery. Shale, limestone, and coal—I would never have come into being without these elemental deposits.

Then, more than half a million years ago, knobby hills, the descendants of once jagged mountains, sprang up around you as the weight of an immense glacier retreated. Reconfigured, flow reversing poles, you transformed. You joined infamous rivers spilling into the wide gulf, continuing out into oceans. When European explorers discovered you, they recognized your value. You became a deep natural highway where flat barges transported raw materials needed to build the fiery Steel City downstream. My ancestors immigrated to western Pennsylvania to begin a new life expending your neighboring resources. Without you, my parents would never have been born near each other. Because of you they met, fell in love, and started a family.

The Allegheny Valley Railroad replaced floating barges, but still, it was you. As a small boy fascinated by trains, my father incessantly asked for car rides to see the station "in town." As a man, a husband and father, he chose this small borough of East Brady, Pennsylvania, to live out the rest of his years. Speeding trains avoided the wildest of your meanders by tunneling through a deep, narrow strip of land. But my father picked the crook of your arm, a place where life moved a little slower, as my playground.

The miracle of your sweeping curves at Brady's Bend creates a geographical wonder. On moonlit nights, low-flying fighter pilots spot it while performing maneuvers without instrumentation. Your tightest embrace creates a close-knit community composed of homegrown townies, exploring passersby, and boaters wowed by bald eagles. We congregate to watch your havoc-wreaking ice jams and to mourn the lives lost to your authority. We stand on the edge of a former hang-gliding launch site, pinpointed near historical markers. From high above, we gaze down on you in awe and document sunsets worthy of a million photographs.

I exist because of you, as do my children, my future grandchildren, and so on, and so on for generations to come. For these priceless gifts you've given I am eternally grateful, my beloved Allegheny River.

Sincerely Yours Forever,
Jennifer

WHERE IT'S NEEDED MOST

Phil Giunta

After dumping a decade's worth of pills into a glass tumbler, Max Everett flicked the last empty prescription bottle across the kitchen table, knocking several others over the edge.

"A brilliant shot. Five hundred points to Everett and..." Max swirled the kaleidoscopic cocktail of vodka, anti-depressants, and anxiolytics. "... game over."

Contrary to the diagnoses of several psychiatrists over the years, Max struggled neither with depression nor anxiety. At least, not his own. It wasn't until his early twenties that he'd realized his prodigious capacity for absorbing the tempestuous emotions of those around him. Of course, all attempts to convince his family of this had proven futile. To placate them, Max had grudgingly accepted the occasional prescriptions, only to toss the unopened bottles into a box tucked in a forgotten corner of his bathroom closet.

Instead, he had turned to daily meditation and a sensory deprivation tank at the local health spa to preserve his sanity amid the incessant buffeting of several thousand unrestrained minds.

Then, the COVID-19 pandemic struck early in the new year, forcing all nonessential businesses to close, including the spa. As months passed under quarantine, the city's population grew restive, anxious. Smoldering tensions fueled long suppressed animosities. The pin was finally pulled from the grenade when an unarmed black man, smoking on his front steps and disturbing no one, was gunned down by two white cops while "resisting arrest."

The following week, a peaceful protest downtown erupted into a night of rioting. The police station was firebombed, shops were looted, and lives lost.

For Max, meditation provided a meager bulwark against the relentless barrage of animus, fear, and rage. The meds he had once rejected now promised a permanent solution. After a few deep breaths, he lifted the tumbler to his mouth, wondering how long it would take for his end to come once he downed the concoction. *The sooner the better.*

From the kitchen counter, his cell phone buzzed. Max lowered the glass until the noise stopped. Mustering his courage after nearly a full minute, he raised it to his mouth once more. His cell phone buzzed again. The caller had left a voicemail.

Chrissake. Max leapt from his chair and snatched the phone from the counter. After listening to the message, he tapped the screen and pressed the phone to his ear.

"Soul of the City, this is Priscilla. How can I help you?"

"Pris, it's Max Everett."

"Max, thanks for calling me back. Did I catch you at a bad time?"

His gaze shifted to the tumbler. "I was just about to take a nap. What's going on?"

"How about a float instead? Not sure if you saw our posts on social media, but we're open again now that the restrictions have been lifted. Since you had a bunch of appointments that were cancelled due to the pandemic, I wanted to let you know we have a slot open at one-thirty today if you're available."

Max closed his eyes and rolled his head back. "Yes! I mean, yeah, I'm available."

"Great! We'll need to take your temperature when you arrive, and you'll have to wear a mask to enter and walk through the spa to your assigned salon."

"No problem. I'll be there. Thank you, Pris." Max rubbed his eyes. *You might've just saved my life.*

An hour later, Max adjusted his sunglasses and N95 mask as the green and white taxi slowed to a stop alongside his building. He opened the back door, tossed his small duffel onto the seat, and climbed in.

"I thought it might be you," the driver said. "I picked you up here just before the pandemic."

"Oh, right. Didn't recognize you with the mask. How are ya?"

"I'm good, bruh. You work out here? I thought all these factories were abandoned."

"Actually, I live here. The owners were willing to rent out the basement cheap while they renovate the building."

"Huh. Kinda remote isn't it?"

"Just the way I like it."

"Guess I can't blame ya. At least you ain't gotta deal with these damn protestors. They keep moving through town, blockin' traffic. Makes drivin' a friggin' nightmare. So where to?"

"Sixth and Ridgemont."

As the cab made its circuitous route through town, Max steepled his fingers and closed his eyes, bracing himself against the torrent of random emotions from the minds they passed along the way. Mild trepidation brushed his thoughts from a distance, giving way to fierce jealousy nearby. Disappointment from one tired old soul faded, to be replaced by youthful lust elsewhere. Max winced as a surge of grief and despair threatened to drown him. He tried to withdraw, throw up a shield, but the raw and desperate passions clawed at his consciousness, then vanished in a burst of—Warmth? Hope? Comfort? All of that, but something more. Love? Could it be? Yes! Love of a purity and intensity the likes of which Max had never before encountered. It washed over him, embraced him, elevated him. He lowered his defenses and allowed it to consume him. *Who are you? I must know. I can feel you fading. Don't leave me...*

With a cry, Max opened his eyes. He threw himself against the passenger door and peered out the window. *Where did that come from?* He slid across the seat, knocking his duffel to the floor, and searched the opposite side of the street until his gaze locked onto Saint Sophie's Hospital. *There...*

"You okay, buddy?" The driver stared at him from the rearview mirror. "Somethin' wrong?"

Max slumped, still catching his breath. "Not at all. Just the opposite, in fact."

I will find you again... whoever you are.

In the pediatric oncology wing at Saint Sophie's Hospital, Nadi Santikos sat hunched before her computer screen at the nurses' station. She barely noticed when one of her colleagues, Jasiri, dropped into the chair beside her. "So, who's your hot date today? Dylan, Aiden, Rajesh, or one of the new kids?"

"Well, it definitely won't be Ashley again." Constance, the senior nurse, leaned over the counter and dropped a file folder onto the desk. "She's being discharged in a few hours. Tumor free as of yesterday."

"And no one knows why," Jasiri added in a low voice. "Doctor Larousse is completely baffled. Ashley's the third kid in two months."

Constance pointed to her. "That's the power of Jesus right there, honey. Ain't nothin' to be baffled about."

Nadi logged off of the computer and rolled her chair back. "All right, chickies. I'll be with Ellen for a little while. I promised I'd read to her before my shift was over."

"You're gonna be a good momma someday," Constance said.

Nadi rolled her eyes.

"I'm serious, girl. You just need to find the right man—after the pandemic is over, of course."

"I don't think there are any good men left in this city." Nadi rounded the nurses' station and made her way down the corridor. She stepped into the last room on the right and approached the bed. Its occupant, an eight-year-old girl whose sandy blonde hair had been lost to chemotherapy, turned her face away from the window as Nadi approached. "Are you here to read to me?"

"As promised." Nadi picked up a book from the corner table and flipped through the pages. "We'll pick up where we left off yesterday."

"I heard Ashley's going home soon. Her cancer went away."

"Yes, that's true."

"I wish I could go home. I sometimes wake up in the middle of the night and I... I'm scared that I'll never be able to go home again. Please don't tell my mom and dad, but I'm scared a lot."

"I won't tell them." Nadi put the book aside. "Ellen, do you trust me?"

"Sure."

With a glance at the open door, Nadi stepped around the bed and closed the privacy curtain.

"What are you doing?"

At Ellen's puzzled gaze, Nadi smiled. "Sending you home. Now, close your eyes and think about... think about everyone you love and everything you loved doing before you got sick." She laid a gentle hand on Ellen's chest. A yellow glow appeared beneath her palm. "Think about all of the places you love to go. The beach, the park..."

Nadi inhaled deeply, held her breath for a few seconds then exhaled. She repeated this a few more times. When she spoke again, her voice was strained. "How do you feel, Ellen?"

"Warm, but... a nice warm. What's happening?"

"Almost done, sweetie."

The yellow glow faded. Nadi lifted her hand. "You can open your eyes now."

"What was that?"

"Two more days and you'll be home, but can you do something for me, Ellen? Promise me you won't tell anyone about this. Will you do that for me?"

"Sure." Ellen nodded.

Nadi felt a trickle along her upper lip. "I'll be right back and then I'll read to you, okay?" She shoved aside the privacy curtain and hurried into the bathroom. Yanking down her mask, Nadi staggered toward the sink. Blood trickled from her right nostril. *That's a first.* She snatched a paper towel from the dispenser and pressed it to her nose.

Idiot. Nadi gazed at her drawn, sallow reflection in the mirror. *Ellen could have waited one more shift. You still haven't recovered from healing Caleb and Ashley. Keep going at this pace, who's going to heal you?*

Max stood in the vestibule at Soul of the City spa and peered up at the wall-mounted temperature scanner. Apparently satisfied that he was virus-free, Pris held up a hole punch. "Do you have your frequent floater card?"

"Oh, yeah. Sorry." Max thumbed through his wallet and produced a tattered blue business card. "Been so long, I forgot." He slipped it under the Plexiglas divider that spanned the length of the reception desk.

As Pris reached for the card, a miasma of anguish, worry, and dread crept into Max's thoughts, jarring him out of the euphoria that still lingered from the cab ride. Whatever troubled her, Pris concealed it well, surgical mask notwithstanding. Her eyes betrayed no hint of sorrow.

She held up the punch card. "Looks like your next float will be free."

"Any chance I could use it today, to extend my session?"

"You want to spend two hours in the tank?"

"After the past four months, I could spend a week in the tank."

Pris swiped a slender finger across the screen of her tablet computer. "You and me both. Yeah, I can put you in for a double session."

"Thanks." Max paused for a beat. "Sorry to be forward, but are you okay? You seem distraught."

"Not at all."

"Pris."

Her shoulders slumped. "Right. Almost forgot I'm talking to the human lie detector." She tossed the tablet onto the counter. "My dad tested positive for COVID-19 a few weeks ago and now he's on a ventilator at Saint Sophie's. They won't let me see him, of course, so here I am, trying to keep my shit together."

"I'm sorry, Pris. I wish..." *I could take your pain away.* Max pressed his open hand to the Plexiglas divider. "I wish there was something I could do."

Eyes glistening, Pris reached across the counter and did likewise. "Thanks, Max. I'm sure all of this has been hell for you, too."

"Nearly enough to drive me to drink."

Pris lowered her hand and reached into a drawer. "You need to find a girl, Max. Get some love in your life to distract you from all the stress."

"Love seems to be a rare commodity in this city." Max mustered a perfunctory smile. "But I'll keep that in mind."

She slipped a keycard under the divider. "Salon D is all yours. You know the drill. Shower first before entering the tank."

"Thanks, Pris. You're a life saver."

"That's two you owe me, but who's counting?"

Although Nadi had wanted nothing more than to go straight home and collapse at the end of her shift, healing Ellen had left her not only enervated but famished. Fortunately, her apartment was only five blocks from Saint Sophie's and her favorite Greek diner just two blocks beyond that. She'd called ahead, allowing ample time for her order to be prepared and ready by the time she arrived. *Ten minutes more and I'll be home, in my pajamas, and chowing down on stuffed grape leaves and moussaka in no ti—*

As she passed an alley, Nadi was nearly trampled by a mob of teenagers, some wielding baseball bats and crowbars, but not one wearing a mask. They bolted across the street and through a parking lot before disappearing out of sight. In their wake, a young black man lay in a fetal position in the middle of the alley.

"Oh my God." Nadi ran to his side and lowered herself to one knee. The boy's left eye was swollen shut. Blood streaked from a gash along his forehead. "I'm a nurse and I'm going to help you. What's your name?"

"Randall," he whispered. "Hard to breathe."

"Does your chest hurt, Randall?"

"Ribs. They... wouldn't stop kickin' me."

Setting aside her purse and takeout bag, Nadi lifted his polo shirt. She placed one hand atop a series of dark purple bruises and the other on the side of his head. "What happened?"

"We were marching... with the protest. Bunch of... white guys came at us with... bats and pipes. Started another riot."

"Yeah, I just ran into some of them. Randall, can you close your eyes for me?"

"What are you gonna do?"

Nadi smiled. "Trust me."

There's nothing better to rejuvenate mind, body, and soul than floating nude atop ten inches of briny water while encased in absolute darkness. Yet, Max would have traded the past two hours of heavenly silence for just five minutes of the euphoria he'd experienced on his way here.

After his session in the sensory deprivation tank, Max called for a cab and waited in the lounge by the window. He chided himself for his suicide attempt even while bracing his mind against the ebb and flow of emotions from the passing throng on the street—annoyance, contempt, fury, comfort, warmth... love!

Max gripped the arms of his chair. Yes. It was the same sensation he'd felt in the cab earlier as they passed Saint Sophie's, only more intense. Closer. Possibly just a few blocks away. Max leapt from his seat and started toward the vestibule when a wave of panic sent him staggering. He nearly toppled into another patron before steadying himself. Outside, a stampede of bodies shoved, weaved, and shouted their way past the windows. Was another riot under way?

With a brusque wave to Pris, Max charged through the door and out to the sidewalk just as a green and white cab pulled up to the curb. Ignoring it, he shrank back against the wall of the spa, glancing right and left. *Goddamn it, which way?* He closed his eyes. After a moment, he allowed a furtive smile. *Of course, love intervenes where it's needed most.*

Max pushed off the wall and plunged into the fray.

In the alley, Nadi collapsed against the wall and pulled a wad of napkins from her takeout bag. She pressed them to her bleeding nose as Randall sat up and gaped at her, all injuries healed. "How did you do that?"

"Ancient Greek healing technique. Runs in the family."

Distant gunfire punctuated the wail of approaching police sirens.

"Shit's about to go down. We gotta move."

"I need a few minutes." Nadi slipped her purse into her takeout bag. "Just go."

Randall shifted his gaze from one end of the alley to the other.

"I'll be fine." Nadi waved her napkin. "Go now. Stay safe, and please quarantine yourself for two weeks. Riots be damned. We're still in a pandemic."

"Yeah. Good luck and thanks again." With that, Randall was gone.

Only a block and a half to home. With one hand on the wall and the other clutching her takeout bag, Nadi started back toward the street, pausing to suss out the scene. Most of the violence was still confined to the next block. As if to confirm this, a pair of ambulances barreled through the nearest intersection and passed again a moment later at the opposite end of the alley behind her. *Please stay over there until I get home.* Nadi shuffled out to the sidewalk, feeling as if she'd aged thirty years in the past ten minutes.

The first gunshot tore through an outdoor display in front of a shop directly beside her.

"Get down!"

As more rounds peppered windows and walls around her, a tall man charged toward her from across the street. Nadi's takeout bag flew from her grasp. She cried out as the impact pushed her to the asphalt at the alley's entrance, but the man had wrapped his arms around her head and back, cushioning the impact.

Nadi's mask slipped down to her chin as she turned her head away from the man's shoulder. She arched her neck but could see little more than huddled bodies in the middle of the street.

"He's down!" someone shouted. "We got his gun."

She patted her savior's back. His shirt was damp with sweat. "Uh, sir? Thank you. I think they got the shooter. We should be okay now. Can we stand up, please?"

With a grunt, the man shifted his weight, but not enough to liberate Nadi. He turned his head to face her. "Only one problem. I can't move my legs."

Nadi brought her hand up. That wasn't sweat. *Oh no...*

"What's your name?"

"Max." He rested his forehead against the asphalt.

"Okay, Max. I'm a nurse and I'm going to help you, but you have to trust me, okay?"

"Do I have a choice?"

"No. I want you to close your eyes and don't try to move until I tell you to. Can you do that for me?"

"Yes."

Despite his condition, Max could sense that this woman was exhausted, filled with trepidation and doubt.

Was she truly the source of the perfect bliss he'd felt earlier, or had he just risked his life for nothing?

Max felt a hand rustle the back of his shirt and a moment later, his own doubts were dispelled as elation coursed through him. Even if he died here and now, it would have been worth it to save this divine being. He turned his head to face her. When he opened his eyes, she was little more than a blur. "Who are you? I have to know."

"I'm Nadi." Her voice was little more than a hoarse whisper. "Now hush. I need to focus. Your injuries are severe."

Blinking away his tears, Max gazed at this angel in blue scrubs. Voluminous brown hair cascaded along the pavement and clung to the sides of her face. Her angular jaw was clenched and her olive complexion damp. They say women don't sweat, they glisten, but Nadi's face glowed in a golden manifestation of the pure, selfless love she radiated.

Her hand slipped from his back. She tossed three spent rounds to the sidewalk. "You... should be fine in a minute." She clenched her teeth, arched her back, and broke down into tears. Her body trembled beneath his.

"Nadi, what's wrong?"

"It hurts." She drew in a sharp breath. Blood trickled from her aquiline nose. "Every time I... heal someone, I... absorb their pain and... you're my third one today. I can't take anymore."

"You won't need to." Max pushed himself up and knelt over her. He brought gentle hands to her temples. "Let me take it. Absorbing pain is my specialty." He closed his eyes. "A burden shared is a burden halved, my dear."

Nadi gasped as she cupped her hands over his. "My God... you're an empath."

"That's what led me to you." Max opened his eyes. "Better now?"

She nodded. Max picked up her purse and helped Nadi to her feet. She fell into him as her legs buckled, and he embraced her. "Can you walk? We need to get out of here."

"I just need a minute." She glanced down at her takeout order strewn across the pavement. "Damn it, that was my dinner."

"I'll buy you dinner. Anything you want."

"After we each quarantine for fourteen days." Nadi pulled back. "Seriously, who are you? How did you really find me, and why would you risk your life for a stranger? You could have been killed."

"You were worth the risk." Max handed over her purse. "As to how I found you, it wasn't hard. Love always intervenes where it's needed most."

THE SURPRISE

Lisa Valli

"**S**urprise!!"

A wave of pride washed over me as I saw the look of pure happiness on my dad's face. We pulled off the perfect surprise, one that came together after many trials and tribulations. I thought back to that hot July day, when I was sitting at the outdoor table with my siblings during our family reunion. One thing you'll never see is an Italian-American family gathered at a table sitting in stumped silence. But that was us, as we tried to figure out what we could get our dad for his upcoming 80th birthday.

"What about new golf clubs?" my brother, Lou, suggested.

"Or a rangefinder for the golf course," my sister, Lynne, tossed out.

"How about a motorized pull cart," my other sister, Laureen said.

Can you tell my dad likes to golf? While these were all nice gifts, none of them felt right.

What do you get for a man who literally has everything? And what do you get for a man whose wife and family is the most important thing in the world to him?

My, father, Angelo Valli was never a materialistic person. He'd worked hard throughout his life, climbing the corporate ladder. In business, he used his middle name, Louis, since Italian-Americans were discriminated against in those days. He reached the highest echelons of a Fortune 100 business, back when people stayed with the same company for their whole lives. He married my mother when he was fresh out of college, and they were together for over fifty years, back when people stayed married to the same person for their whole lives.

They met at The Ice Plant, a local dance hall that had previously made and distributed ice to the neighboring towns. On the weekends, The Ice Plant was the place to be. It boasted a jukebox and rows of booths flanked the dance floor where giggling co-eds would sit and watch the dancers, while sipping sodas and root beer floats.

On one such Saturday night, both my mother and father were at The Ice Plant. He was captivated the moment he saw Frances Kurilko. But as he watched her, he realized they were polar opposites as far as their personalities were concerned. She was an outgoing, brilliant woman with a mane of raven hair and ocean green eyes, bubbling around the dance floor with her friends.

He was broody and handsome in his black leather jacket. His friends urged him to ask her to dance, knowing he was an introvert so he would never do it of his own accord. He hemmed and hawed and told them to knock it off. Finally, his friend Shug thrust him forward as she was dancing nearby. He bumped into her. After he threw Shug a look that said, "I'm going to kill you!" he turned to her and searched for something to say.

"Hi there," he finally mumbled. "Wanna dance?" He reached his hand toward her.

"Of course," she laughed, as she grabbed the offered hand and dragged him onto the dance floor.

She told me later she'd seen him there on other occasions and had been wishing for him to speak to her. To her, he was the definition of "dark and handsome." Not so much in the "tall" category, but she didn't mind.

"Where are you from?" she asked as they jitterbugged.

"Nemacolin," he said as he spun her in an underarm turn. "And you?"

"Bobtown. I go to Point Marion High School. I'm a Sophomore. And you?"

"Carmichaels High. Senior," he said as he performed the perfect rock step. She was thrilled that he was such a good dancer. Her eyes sparkled as she followed him perfectly, not missing a beat.

Nemocolin and Bobtown were small coal mining towns in southwestern Pennsylvania. Both were too small to have their own high school so they each had to travel over twenty miles.

Their relationship took off from that first night at the Ice Plant. She cheered him on at his football games, spent afternoons together after school at the soda shop, and before they knew it, she was attending his high school graduation.

Just when he was set to leave for college, my dad went to my mom's house to break up with her. In his mind, there was no way the relationship would work while she was still in high school and he was miles away at college.

After he left, my mom sank onto the couch, devastated, tears rolling down her cheeks. Not even ten minutes had passed before she heard a knock on her door.

She opened it to see my dad, who was torn up. He couldn't go through with it. They stayed together, never to be parted again.

They had four children, starting with my brother, then me and my two sisters. To me, it always seemed like the perfect number in the perfect family. We never ceased to feel our parents' strong love surrounding us and keeping us close.

Strong family bonds run in the family. My father was one of six children in an Italian immigrant family. His parents literally came over on "the boat" so my grandparents could start a new life in the U.S. My grandfather, who we called Nonno, worked long hours underground in a coal mine in southwestern Pennsylvania to provide for his growing family. Nonna worked tirelessly cooking, cleaning, and raising their six children. Her dream was for all her children to attend college. Once my dad and his siblings got older, the family moved to Pittsburgh where they all attended the University of Pittsburgh.

They bought a large house with four floors within walking distance to the University. Nonna ran her kitchen with the discipline of a five-star general. She used the kitchen table to make homemade pasta, creating tagliatelle, spaghetti, and lasagna.

My favorite, though, was and still is cappelletti. Cappelletti means "little hat" in Italian. It is rather labor intensive, so a team had to be assembled to make it.

To an American who has never had it, cappelletti would be most similar to tortellini—a filled pasta which is then folded into a shape. In our case, it was filled with ground veal, lemon zest and cream cheese. The pasta was cut into a square, filled and then folded into a little hat, which looked more like a scarf tied around someone's head. My aunts would surround the table, while Nonna prepared the pasta. That tradition carried on to my family where we would surround my mother as she kneaded the pasta and fed it through her pasta machine.

We would then take turns doing our part. My sister, Laureen, would separate the layers of pasta squares that came out of the machine and give them to my dad, who would dab the filling on each individual square. He would pass it to me to do the first pat and fold and finally to Lou, who made the final twist, finishing the "hat." Lynne, the youngest, was responsible for counting them and lining them up on large trays before my dad slid them into the freezer. They went in for a flash freeze, and were then transferred into freezer bags, usually in groups of fifty to a hundred.

"Stop eating it!" I admonished my brother, as he snuck one into his mouth when Mom wasn't looking. Then I'd pop one in my mouth and we would both burst out laughing.

"Hey, you two! That's one less for each of your bowls," Mom would say firmly.

The cappelletti was slowly simmered in homemade chicken broth. This soup was served at Christmas dinner before the main meal. Because of the time it took to make, we only had it once a year and the amount of cappelletti you got in your bowl was rationed because we often had over thirty people at Nonna's house.

Often times there were cousins, aunts or uncles who were in town visiting from Italy. They loved to be at my grandparents' place to experience a real American Christmas. Nonno and Nonna still kept in close touch with all the relatives in Italy and would visit them from time to time. I remember they took my parents with them on one of their trips in the late '60s. They were gone for two weeks. It was the longest I had ever been away from my parents and I missed them terribly.

As we ate dinner together after their return, they shared details of their trip including the wonders at the Vatican such as the Pieta and the Sistine Chapel. My mom shared the high points of Florence, Venice and Rome. While they loved visiting the big cities, their favorite part of the trip was going to the town of Sant' Agata Feltria in northern Italy. We still had relatives there. My dad was especially happy to reconnect with his cousin Arrigo.

Nonno was the brother of Arrigo's mother. My dad and Arrigo looked like brothers, although Arrigo's hair was sandy blond while my father's was a chestnut brown. They both had the same warm brown eyes that expressed compassion and love. They met Arrigo's wife Paola and his two children, Beatrice (pronounced Bea-tree-chay) and Francesco.

My dad spent most of his free time with Arrigo. They enjoyed lazy afternoons drinking homemade wine near a vineyard and taking walks through the winding cobblestone streets of the town.

Italians have difficulty saying a name with only one syllable, so my mom quickly became Francesca and my dad was Angelo.

Arrigo was mayor of Sant' Agata and was the perfect tour guide to show them around. On the two weekends that my parents were there, they went to the outdoor market in the center of town, where they perused luscious fresh produce, homemade pasta, and bottles of homemade Verdicchio and Sangiovese. They sampled Italian pastries that nearly melted on their tongues.

While my mom and Paola shopped, my dad and Arrigo lounged in an outdoor café sipping espresso, conversing in Italian. My dad was a bit rusty at first, but once he got into the habit of speaking the language again, it all came back to him. Of course, they didn't want to leave Italy, but they missed us.

Once home, they regaled us with stories of the wonderful time they'd had, and my dad made a promise. "We will return and we're going to take you all with us! A Salut!" he toasted us with his wine glass.

And years later, he kept that promise. My parents took all four of us to Italy. We got to experience everything they had and more! Seeing the statue of David in Florence, the Trevi Fountain in Rome, and gliding in a gondola through the canals of Venice is something I will remember for the rest of my life.

We went to Sant' Agata and met the people we had been hearing about for years. Arrigo's daughter Beatrice was now married and had two children of her own, seven-year-old Alessia, and Giacomo, who was three.

We laughed at Arrigo chasing after Giacomo saying, "Basta! Cattivo! Cattivo!" which means "bad, bad." The nickname was well earned.

Everyone knows the food in Italy is incredible, but I wasn't prepared for the overwhelming portions, or the fact that the courses kept coming, one after another. A favorite memory was our first lunch at a small café in the square. To my utter delight, they served us heaping bowls of cappelletti. The aroma of the steaming soup transported me right back to Nonna's kitchen. I thought I had died and gone to heaven, especially when they came back out with big pots and huge ladles to refill our bowls.

Next was a pasta course of tagliatelle with a light tomato sauce, a meat course of braised venison seasoned with rosemary, grilled vegetables (zucchini, asparagus, carrots and squash), followed by a tray of cheeses. The meal concluded with bowls filled with summer fruits and a salad at the end.

After he had finished the first two courses of soup and pasta, I remember Lou patted his stomach and said, "Whew, I'm really full!"

In the next second, his eyes nearly popped out of his head when the large tray of venison was set down right in front of him.

At every meal it was the same. Fabulous food and unlimited homemade wine.

Sometimes, I would sit next to Arrigo during our meals. A true Italian, Arrigo, would gesticulate with large hand motions as he told vivid stories of our history and his life in Italy. He was a teacher at a town nearby and spoke English, Italian, and was fluent in French. I'd studied French in school, and we attempted to converse while sampling various Italian wines. Actually, he did most of the conversing. I just tried to keep up and throw in a word here or there. Of course, the more wine I drank, the more unintelligible my French became.

We spent our days in Sant' Agata seeing the sights. First ambling across the vineyards, surveying the land where Nonno had grown wine, then saying a prayer in the pews of the little church where my grandparents had gotten married. And we even danced on the stage of the old theater, while my parents took pictures of us from one of the loges that extended out from the first balcony.

We toured La Roca, an old castle at the very top of the mountain in the town. The view from the summit was incredible. Arrigo took us to the railing outside the castle and pointed out the towns that dotted the hills and valleys below us. A small white church with a pointed steeple gleamed against the green grass of the rolling hills. He shared stories and anecdotes about the people he knew in many of the villages.

My gaze was drawn back to the streets of Sant' Agata, just below us. I watched an older woman wearing a red babushka and a long dark skirt, pumping the handle of a well as water trickled into her bucket and I realized how far away I was from my suburban life in Pittsburgh. In more ways than one.

One of my standout memories was Alessia's communion. She was dressed in a long white gown and wore a ring of flowers on her head like all the other girls. The boys were dressed the same, except for the crown of flowers. The children entered the church in a single file line, each carrying a lit candle. I knelt at the pew and thanked God that I was blessed enough to be in Italy with all of my extended relatives sharing in this incredible experience.

Beautiful hymns, sung in Italian, filled the church. Candles flickered at the altar and lined the outer sides of the sanctuary. The pungent smell of incense, burning near the altar, infiltrated the air.

Once the ceremony ended, the children left the church in an orderly fashion. I gathered my things from the pew, assuming it was all over. After the children walked out, however, their fathers, who were clad in burgundy robes adorned with gold braiding, followed them. Outside the church they picked up a gold canopy called the *baldacchino*. It was a beautiful piece of fabric that the children gathered under, as their fathers surrounded them, and they all walked together.

We followed them and strolled through the town. The residents lined the streets cheering on the procession. They had put flower petals in front of their doors in various shapes. First, I saw a chalice configured of marigold petals. Then there was a dove made of white carnation sprigs. Next an angel. The fact that the whole town participated in this event struck me with a poignancy that still rests within me today.

As with any vacation, it was time to go home. I remember seeing tears in my father's eyes saying good-bye to everyone, not knowing when he would see them again.

Which brings me back to the summer of 2012, with my siblings trying to decide what to get my dad for his 80th birthday.

As we sat there looking at each other, all our suggestions falling flat between us, a thought popped into my mind and I blurted out, "Arrigo!" They all looked at me and without even a question, my sister Lynne asked, "Can we pull it off?"

Our surprise would be to fly Arrigo in for the celebration. We only had a month and we would have to involve our mom since she was planning the party.

Once our idea was set, we hit our first snag, Arrigo was afraid to fly. He'd never flown overseas. Our Italian cousin, Leonardo, had traveled many times to Miami for business. Arrigo agreed to come, if he could fly with Leonardo. I booked flights for both of them, hardly able to contain my excitement.

The next day, however, I got a message from Leonardo saying that due to work obligations, he wouldn't be able to make the trip. My heart sank. Our wonderful surprise was ruined. I called Beatrice to discuss the situation.

"Bea, I'm so sorry but Leonardo can't make the trip because of work. I'm so disappointed. It would mean so much to my dad to have your father here."

Bea told me to hold on. Arrigo was at her house. I heard muffled voices in the background and then Bea came back on the phone.

"He says he will come!" she said, excitement in her voice.

"What? Really? That's wonderful!" I nearly shouted.

One month later, my husband and I picked Arrigo up at the Pittsburgh International Airport. He stayed at our house. We had to keep him undercover until the party the next night.

The next evening we drove to the restaurant with Arrigo in the back seat. It was a beautiful evening and I still remember the way the sun shone across Arrigo's face, his smile beaming with anticipation.

The cocktail hour had already started when we walked in. Arrigo was hiding in a separate room. My children were there along with my nieces and nephews. My brother and sisters and their spouses were nervously sipping wine, trying to contain their enthusiasm. My dad's siblings were present with their spouses as well, oblivious to what would happen next.

When it came time to make a toast, we all stood in front of my father, and I read my prepared remarks. I talked about what a wonderful father he was and how he had impacted all of our lives. I talked about the importance of family and of all the wonderful memories that we had shared with him. I mentioned all the vacations we had gone on over the years.

But I told him that best of all, we appreciated the trips to Italy. He had taken the four of us first, and then a couple of trips with our spouses and finally a trip with all the grandchildren. A total of five trips in all. I thanked him for giving us that wonderful gift and opportunity to experience another world and to meet all our relatives.

I told him that as a thank-you for all he'd done for us, we had flown in "a very special bottle of wine from Italy just for him."

A man entered the room carrying a bottle held high in front of his face. It laid horizontally across his hands. My dad, assuming it was the maître d', stared at the wine as it was carried across the room.

As the man got closer, Arrigo lowered the wine, so my dad could see his face.

My heart clutched as I saw the wave of recognition wash over my father's face. His eyes lit with joy and in the next second, filled with tears. He was so shocked and overcome, he could barely contain himself. He hugged Arrigo in disbelief.

My mother teared up as well, and held her clasped hands to her lips, delighted with my father's reaction.

We had succeeded! We had pulled off the ultimate surprise!

My dad told me later that there was no gift that could match this. It was the best birthday present he ever had.

And looking back, I'm so glad that we did what we did. So proud we went to the extra effort to make it happen. That ended up being his last birthday. The following month my dad was diagnosed with esophageal cancer. He died nine months later.

As I finish the words on this page, I notice on my computer that today is August seventh. It's my dad's birthday.

SASSY SERA

N. J. Hammer

She was only ten weeks old when she came to live with us. Even in those early days she was sweet and easy, not fussy or easily irritated. Since she didn't come with a moniker, we chose Sera simply because it suited her princess personality.

Just like any other baby, Sera loved to play with everything. Cool green grass fascinated her. At first she tried to eat it, but it wasn't long before she discovered the joy of just lying on her back on a warm summer's day and watching the clouds scuttle by. Her favorite outside game was chasing birds. They seemed to enjoy it too, waiting until she almost reached them before flying off into a nearby tree where they'd tease her with a twittering laugh.

Going for a walk down the street was another favorite pastime. The faster the movement, the better. Her head constantly turning from side to side, she took note of everything. Not shy, she often said hello to the neighbors in her own unique style.

Playing ball was a fun activity both outside and in the house. Her daddy was much better than me at throwing and catching the ball. That's when we discovered Sera was a southpaw.

I was best at reading to her. Sera would stretch out on the sofa, put her head in my lap and listen intently as I gently massaged her back. It didn't seem to matter what kind of story I recited as long as my voice was soft, and my hand kept moving.

Sera wasn't too picky an eater. She would try anything, but as she got older her delicate digestive system became apparent. One thing she hated was peas. Somehow she managed to eat a whole bowl of homemade stew and leave the peas sitting in the bottom of the dish.

She was two years old when her hip problem became obvious. We hadn't been warned of such a possibility, but after investigating her heritage we learned we shouldn't have been surprised. Unfortunately, there wasn't anything medical science could do to help.

That was the beginning of many health problems. As she grew older her walk became slower and running became difficult and painful. All too quickly she could no longer keep up with the others in the neighborhood, but that didn't seem to faze her. She stayed as sassy as ever and we continued to love and pamper her.

We only had the honor of knowing Sera for twelve years. Her delicate physical health got worse quickly and when the joy left her life we let her go.

She was and always will be the best dog ever!

LOVE IS

Judy England–McCarthy

L**ove is a chance encounter with someone after your soul has given up.**

"You seem like a nice guy, but nothing personal, I think all men are assholes," I said, quite elated and proud of myself. It was both direct and honest and I felt covered the whole gamut. It would dissuade this man sitting across from me from pursuing me any further. The house party was in full swing and no one else heard what had been said. I was in a dark place, having just come off a bad relationship, which I only recently found out was a pack of lies. I was in no mood to give any guy the time of day, let alone false hope.

Love is a new beginning.

Too absorbed in my self-satisfaction, having made what I thought was a scintillating comment, I was unexpectedly surprised when I saw his reaction. Before, I hadn't been looking directly at the sandy, curly-haired man across the kitchen table. For the first time I saw his deep penetrating stare and his brown hazel eyes. It was as though my words ignited an interest. "The game was afoot," as Sherlock

Holmes would say. "The gauntlet had been thrown. Challenge accepted."

Love is finding out being different makes the difference.

The man I came to know as Tim was also the best friend of my sister's husband, and we were thrown together fairly often. At first, I figured I was presented with an ideal opportunity to demonstrate just how ill-suited we were. At this time my sister had gutted her main floor and the rooms were stripped to their beams. This allowed for clear sightlines from the kitchen to the other end of the house. Whenever I could, I would do improvisational dancing— visualize a dancing pantomime. I would throw myself into my self-expression with total abandonment. History has shown that people usually think I am on drugs, crazy or both. I later found out from Tim, rather than being a deterrent, it reminded him of his cool sister Sandy who was always doing things out of the norm. Once again my aims to dissuade him were unknowingly forms of some bizarre mating ritual I was unknowingly participating in.

Love is an unexpected joy that touches your heart.

Fast forward several months. A relationship of sorts began to develop partly due to a physical attraction... also, just sheer tenacity on his part to outlast my resistance. We both seemed to possess indomitable wills, and he was like an unrelenting wave against my solid rock, slowly softening my resolve.

A major turning point was a winter's evening when we were both at my sister's house and stepped outside. A light frosting of fresh snow gently coated the ground as we walked a few steps side by side down the road. Without warning he stopped and bent down. Using the side of his palm, he formed a "human bare footprint" and with his fingers drew the toes in the snow-covered pavement in front of their neighbor's garage. He then added a plus sign. Without thinking I followed suit beside his footprint and created a smaller version with my palm and fingers. Had he left it there I don't think it would have touched my heart as deeply. It would have been perceived as a nice romantic gesture. Instead, he bent down again and added another plus sign and a still smaller footprint beside mine. Time seemed to elongate as a deep part of my heart opened like some burgeoning liberated sluice gate. I was so touched that he was envisioning a family with me. Our own "Three Little Bears" just like in the fairy tale. Without talking we silently walked back inside, taking those few steps now hand in hand.

Love is passion's first flame.

Lots of squeaky beds and passionate lovemaking took place after that. We couldn't get enough of each other. As those of you who have traversed love's path know, you don't get the Ying without the Yang. Our first real obstacle took place that summer. The glow of love's first kiss was long gone and now pure logistics took their toll on our budding relationship. Neither of us had a car. He lived in Toronto's East York area, but I lived in the Beaches. This meant two bus rides, or a very long bike ride.

I remember it was a clear summer's day and he had cycled down to my neck of the woods. We were sitting at a picnic table and could see the boats moored at Ash Bridges Bay nearby. It seemed so commonplace, people walking their dogs, children playing in the grass. He sat close as he said, "It wasn't going to work, getting together was too much effort." It is funny how your brain can hear words, but your heart refuses to accept their meaning. Suddenly, the threat to myself became real, a palatable thing. It felt like the time I was winded with a basketball. I sat there motionless, unable to grasp for the much needed air, let alone the words to stop this from happening. I remember I focused my attention on a father with his son, who was showing the boy how to hold a fishing pole at the nearby pier as he spoke. Thinking that everything seemed so normal, as I sat listening to my world inexplicably being broken apart.

Love is a promise of forever.

We still saw each other after that, but had the universe not interceded, I know I wouldn't be writing this love story. Fate had other plans, because, shortly after this, a car manifested for us. My brother-in-law was trading up and selling his old Honda Civic. It needed some work, but the price was right. Suddenly, seeing each other wasn't a problem anymore. But the ardor of the first few months morphed into contentment and routine. Then came my acceptance to the American Academy of Dramatic Arts summer program in NYC. The decision to stay together suddenly became tenuous with the thought of a new adventure awaiting me. Just as suddenly, a ring was being given on bended knee, surrounded by nature, with a promise of forever.

Love is embracing what comes next.

A commitment, once made, is a hard thing to break. But young blood without physical touch to reassure each other and "Ma Bell" being our mainstay of keeping connected, with the odd letters thrown in, was stretching the bond of our vows. Our phone calls, first upbeat, soon became random, disjointed and heart breaking. Caught up in NYC adventure, the pauses got longer. Angry words and recriminations began to seep into our dialogue. Once again when things might have ended, he showed up unexpectedly in NYC. The surprise weekend together, reconnecting and being able to share my new world, firsthand, once again changed our storyline. Hope sprang alive once more.

Love is sharing the great unknown.

Then came innumerable classes, learning lines, plays, and discovering who I was and who I wanted to be. Soon the adventure was over, or so I thought. But life had other plans. Returning home broke, tired and at a loss as to what I was to do next, I received a letter in the mail saying I had been selected as a Canadian to immigrate to the USA.

"Where do we go from here?" I heard myself asking my fiancé.

I was holding the letter that required an answer, that would, one way or the other change our lives forever. We had barely weathered my time away and a few short paragraphs were forcing us to choose to commit further, or walk away. It is no small thing to ask a man who has never ventured out of his Ontario province, to begin a new life, in a new country, with nothing but a dream to offer. It was decided we would do this adventure together. Youth is resilient, but time and circumstance would see just how resilient we were.

Love is crossing a border to share a new life together.

Eight weeks was all we had to get married, and then a little over a month after that to get the innumerable documents together to cross the border into our new life together. In the interim I had somehow come across a magazine article about jumping out of a plane and mentioned it to my husband-to-be. He totally embraced the idea for our wedding day and the next thing I knew we were planning it. Not an easy feat with so little time, especially finding a minister who would be willing to marry us up in a plane that was only big enough to hold the pilot and the wedding party, all crammed like sardines, until we said "I do" then jumped.

Love is being crazy enough to jump out of a plane together.

In order to jump out of a plane on our wedding day we needed to pass our certification. This meant learning how to put on and take off the harness, pull the cord and repack the parachute correctly, as well as countless other things. The hardest part for me was falling correctly. Tim got the knack after about three tries. It took me closer to eight tries and the instructor was threatening to fail me if I didn't soon master the skill. Falling correctly meant climbing up about ten stairs to a six by six wooden platform, then hurling yourself off and tuck rolling as you impacted the ground with your equipment on. Doing it wrong was painful, and subjecting myself over and over was a testimonial to my staying power during difficult times.

The sky was clear of clouds that day, and together, yet alone, without preamble, we jumped to pass our certification. As we each pushed against the pressure of the wind to release ourselves from the plane traveling at an altitude of 10,000 feet to freefall for all of thirty seconds. There was a hush after the rush of the push, and then the click and swing when the chute released. Tim went first, then I joined him in the air. The ground lay like a patchwork quilt and its beauty was indescribable. I remember it distinctly, as though etched into my soul.

I landed without a hitch and was so proud of myself that I forgot to grab my chute, like you're supposed to. A wind almost caught up the chute and if it had I would have been dragged along. Later I learned Tim had to employ his second chute as his first parachute didn't automatically open when he ejected from the plane. We both could have had a very uncomfortable end to such an awe inspiring beginning.

Love is a farmer's field surrounded by family and friends.

It was a sunlit autumn day, September 9th, 1989, when we took our vows with the four of us all geared up in our parachute gear. My chute would open up with a Canadian flag motif and I was looking forward to seeing it as I floated down from the sky. But, alas, though it was sunny, and cloudless, we did not get to go up because of the high winds. Instead we shared our words to each other in a farmer's field. Our minister had forgotten that we were to say our own vows and had my husband-to-be recite the normal "Love, honor and cherish."

But when he got to me, I recited the lines I had written from my heart to the man I loved. "I promise to inspire and create a universal bond which neither time nor fate can wither away," I said interrupting the minister midstride. Soft laughter was heard; everyone knew I was just being me.

The rest of the ceremony went without a glitch. I had told everyone my dress was off-white and underplayed it to even my fiancé. So it was a grand surprise later, when I walked into the reception hall in an Elizabethan wedding gown and my maid of honor wore a lady-in-waiting costume piece. Both were a rentals from an Opera company, mine a beautiful cream and hers a lovely sapphire.

Love is letting go of the past to open up a way for the future.

It takes quite a bit to become a resident in another country... from police reports and birth certificates, to x-rays for TB and start-up money, to gainful employment and a place to reside. It may be fate, but fulfilling your destiny is plain hard work and lots of help is certainly part of the equation. The day we left I thought we looked like the Beverly Hillbillies. We had our lives loaded up in a 1978 Ford 150 pickup truck.

Everything was on a list to hand to customs agents when we reached the border. With the truck loaded to the hilt we headed off on the 401 from Toronto to the 1000 Islands border only to find out from U.S. Customs that you can't bring a broken WWII rifle, even if it is a family memento. We either had to backtrack to Gananoque, a drive of about thirty minutes, and have it destroyed at the police station, or return all the way home to leave it there. This would mean regrouping and starting off again the next day. It was my husband's call as it was a relic of his father's, a Green Beret Special Forces operative. Not being a gun fan in general, he opted to destroy the rifle. We were lucky that it hadn't been packed away somewhere in the abyss, also known as all our worldly goods, but behind the seat up front with us. The whole process only delayed us about an hour.

Love is a truck full of hopes and dreams.

When we returned with the documentation proving we had destroyed the weapon, we then handed over our paperwork and were given our resident alien cards and new social security numbers. By the time they input my information and issued my social security number, my husband's was two numbers greater, not one. Someone, somewhere else had already come between us—at least our numbers, that is. As excited as I was to start my new life in America, I was just relieved to finally be out the Customs door and on our way. We hoped to cross into New York State and then head for New Jersey. It was to be our launching off point. We would stay with my mom's brother and his wife. Blessed, they opened both their home and hearts to us.

Love is all there is.

Marriage is sharing all there is with someone else.

My dreams of becoming a famous actress never reached fruition. Over the years I have held many jobs, from insurance clerk, catering server, councilor for the chronically mentally ill, holistic massage therapist, workshop facilitator, School RN, actor, mime, poet, writer and professional storyteller. It is now over thirty years since we said "I do" on a farmer's field and throughout it all, my husband and I have shared it together. We have loved, fought, laughed, cried, raised a son, survived Super Storm Sandy and even now the COVID-19 pandemic together. He has been the candle to my flame. His steadfastness has been the base from which I launch myself into my next flight of fancy.

I look back and see the irony of our life together. Little did I know, my first words uttered to this man would be, "You seem like a nice guy, but nothing personal, I think all men are assholes." Now I know clearly, and deep within my heart, that the last words I will speak to my loyal friend will be, "I love you, and thanks ever so much for sharing this journey with me."

FIRE AND ICE

Kim Pierson

The bunker's fan units were set to maintain a steady 108° F, just on the edge of bearable. It got hotter when the doors opened to let out patrols, and—if all went well—to let them back in again. Two people patrolled every evening, after dark, when the outside was cooler. Even so, they had to wear protective cooling suits, suits that were becoming less reliable. All of which made patrol one of the many jobs no one wanted.

No one except Stella's dad. He volunteered every night.

Back when they'd moved to the bunker, the Council had assured her parents it contained enough resources to survive for fifty years. But barely four years later, things were starting to wear out. The suits. The fans. The people.

Even the animals. The bunker had been a bit like Noah's Ark in the beginning, pairs of goats and chickens and rabbits kept for food or science. Most of them were dead now, had died almost as soon as the Council slammed shut the massive drum-shaped steel door to the outside. Animals don't do well trapped underground.

People don't either, Stella had learned. Some of them had died, too. Others had gone crazy with the knowledge that they couldn't get out.

For Stella's mom, though, it had been a breech baby and a doctor who didn't know the first thing about performing a C-section. And for her baby brother, it had been the wet nurse's milk drying up. All the planning, all the technology to keep this place functioning, and no one had thought to stock a sufficient supply of baby formula.

The rabbits were what pulled Stella through. They, at least, she had the power to save. Caring for them was her contribution to the bunker's future, which was considerably more than its resident fraternity of scientists—the exclusive club to which her family had stolen the secret handshake—had expected.

Everyone knew why the Olsons were there, and it wasn't because they were useful. Back in the 2020s, Stella's grandmother had helped fund the place, inspired it, even. Her book—a romance novel about two teenagers trapped underground as the Earth died around them—had served as a rough plan for the bunker, and for the future. In return, Grams had been awarded four spaces here. When the time came.

People with money had tried to buy their way in, back when they'd finally accepted that there was no way to stop the warming, but by then it was too late. Every space in the bunker was filled with scientists whose skills would sustain the bunker for up to fifty years.

And the Olsons.

Grams had given her spots to the three of them. Three, with the fourth to follow in about six months. Someone new to look forward to, to break up the monotony of bunker-life. And who knew? Maybe the fourth Olson would turn out to be someone who actually had something to offer in terms of helping to run the bunker—or fixing the climate issues that had stranded them there in the first place.

But Harry never had a chance.

Stella couldn't help but wonder if Grams would have done things differently had she known that Stella's mom and Harry would die that first year.

Her dad certainly would have.

After the wet nurse's milk had given out, he'd done everything he could to escape. He'd known there had to still be baby formula out there somewhere—something, or someone, that could save his son. And damned if he wasn't going to get it, or die trying.

But the doors to the outside were locked for the entire first year. No exceptions.

After her father's third attempt to get past the locking mechanism, the Council moved him to the high-security wing, an area they used for people with claustrophobia—the only other ones desperate enough to try to break out of the bunker.

Then someone—Carla Dayton, probably—suggested twelve-year-old Stella was too young to be left unsupervised, and at the last minute, they'd thrown her in, too.

But for the fact that the door locked from the outside, the cell appeared almost exactly like their regular room. The main difference was the wailing of the people in the cells that surrounded theirs, the ones who had lost their minds in the confined space of the bunker. It was Stella's constant background music, varying only in pitch and intensity.

Stella still woke from nightmares with that sound in her head. But she'd pulled through—better than her father. The whole time they were there, the only time he even spoke was when one of the nurses showed up with Harry. They'd brought him every day, and Stella and her father had held him for hours, smelling his sweet baby-ness, her dad singing him lullabies. Harry had slept, mostly. They'd given him something so he would.

And then Harry died, and the Council decided it was safe to release them.

If Harry had been born only six months later, the Council could have sent out a team, maybe found some old containers of formula somewhere. But that first year, they didn't dare open the doors.

Not until they were sure everyone outside was dead.

After Stella and her dad were released, most people kept their distance. One or two kids sent sympathetic glances Stella's way, risking the wrath of Carla Dayton, but only Carla's brother accepted her back as if nothing had ever happened.

Carla'd had it in for Stella from the day they'd met, eight months earlier. All children aged seven to eighteen had to attend classes, and the very first class was on maintenance of the high-speed fan units that cooled the bunker.

"What a shame they didn't have all this technology twenty years ago," Stella had mused aloud, her fingers gliding over the protective screen. "Maybe we could have stopped the warming—slowed it at least. Maybe we wouldn't be here now."

The others probably would have just rolled their eyes and let it drop had Carla not spoken up. The daughter of the head of the Council, Carla thought she ran the place. "Jesus, are you really that dense? They've had this technology for fifty years, at least. They just didn't promote it. No money in it."

Everyone laughed, and Stella's eyes teared up.

It wasn't that her feelings had been hurt. She didn't care what Carla thought—what any of the kids thought. But she was devastated by the notion that people really hadn't been willing to make their lives a tiny bit harder so that their children and grandchildren might have a world to live in.

She left, straight for the comfort and solitude of the rabbit hutches.

Somehow, Dave found her. He introduced himself, which was silly since of course she knew who he was.

"Sorry about my sister," he said. "She was dropped on her head as a child."

"You don't have to apologize for her."

"Ah, but I do. See, I was the one who dropped her. Or so goes the family legend, at least."

"Well done, then."

Dave laughed. And he stayed. They walked together as she checked on Number Three's new litter.

"Carla just doesn't know you, that's all. And to her—to most of us, really—anything unknown is a threat. Everyone else here we practically grew up with. But no one knows anything about you, or your parents." He paused a moment as Stella poked around at the loose bedding Three had made into a nest for her babies. "Like this," he said, gesturing. "How do you know so much about rabbits?"

Stella shrugged. "My grandparents had property in Alaska. They purchased it right after Grams' book became a bestseller, but didn't move there until around 2035—a few years before I was born. My parents stayed behind. They hadn't bought into the whole warming thing. People pretty much thought my grandmother was a crackpot back then—that someone would surely come up with technology that would fix everything before it got too bad."

Dave nodded at that, and Stella felt silly for even mentioning it. He knew full well what people had thought.

"Grams and Grandpa lived mostly off the grid," she continued, wanting to get back to her story before he lost interest. "Kind of like here. They used only solar and wind energy, made their own food, hung their laundry on a clothesline, all of that. Except Grams had a weakness for Diet Coke, and we all had to pretend not to notice when once a month she biked back from town with a couple of two liters hidden under a cloth in her basket."

"You're kidding."

Stella grinned. "No, really. It's one of my favorite memories of her. We moved there in '44. We'd gone to Canada first, when it got too hot in Virginia and the flooding started, and then Mom and Dad finally had to admit that Grams had been right all along. Once we got there, we took over working her garden, and helping with the rabbits."

"So your parents were farmers?"

"Oh, no. My dad's a writer, like my grandma—his mother. Mom paints. Landscapes, mostly. Back when there used to be a landscape to paint."

"No way—a writer and a painter."

He didn't sound judgmental, only surprised. Still.

"There are more things in heaven and earth, David, than are dreamt of in your sciences," Stella said, then added, "That's Shakespeare. Except the 'sciences' part. It's supposed to be 'philosophy'."

"Ah, Shakespeare. I think I may have heard of him," Dave said, so mildly that she immediately felt bad.

"I have a book of his plays," she offered. "It's what I brought in my box. That and some pictures of home."

This time Dave looked impressed. "That's what you packed? A book?"

Each person entering the bunker had been able to bring with them whatever personal items they wished, as long as they fit into a box that was one foot in width and height, two feet in length. It didn't hold a lot, once you added clothing and shoes, but there wasn't much space in the bunker.

Stella nodded. "They have his complete works in the library, but mine's more manageable. If you ever want to borrow it."

But Dave never asked to, and she didn't offer again.

In the four years that had passed since that day, Stella had increasingly wished she'd known ahead of time about the library and what was inside. She might have brought a different book, one that wasn't already there. Maybe even Grams', which had provided seed money for the bunker so long ago.

Her father said the library had been added at Grams' insistence, and as Stella perused the shelves in the small room, she often considered her grandmother's choices. Had she picked those books to entertain, or to educate, or to serve as a time capsule of sorts? Perhaps it was simply that the thought that the works of Zora Neale Hurston and Jane Austen might never again be read left the same sick feeling in Grams' stomach as it did Stella's.

She wondered if her grandmother had known for

certain that there were other bunkers, exactly as she had envisioned in her novel. Other survivors, who might have saved more books. Chosen different music. Preserved additional works of art.

Stella had only learned as much last month, and then only because Dave had chosen to tell her. He'd given her the world when he'd taken her to the radio room and proven they weren't the last people alive on Earth.

Dr. Dayton never allowed any discussion of the possibility of life outside their bunker, and until that day, Stella had no idea a radio room even existed, the entrance hidden away at the rear of a storage closet. Hardly anyone had authorization to enter, but Dave did, and since he'd taken her there, the two of them had returned whenever they could to listen to the other bunkers communicate using the underground radio system.

Not their bunker, though. Never them. Dave said it was because the Council was convinced it was only a matter of time before those other bunkers ran out of supplies and started attacking each other. So they maintained complete radio silence.

Even when the SOS messages started coming.

Stella and Dave were there, listening, as the first one came across. A bunker further north needed parts. Their fan units were dying. Their bunker was an oven, and they were slowly baking in it.

"We have to tell your dad," Stella had insisted. "We have to find a way to help."

But Dave only shook his head, a haunted look in his eyes. "My dad thinks the calls are tricks. That someone's trying to smoke out the bunkers that are left so they can track us down and take over. The rest of the Council agrees. They think we have to look after our own first."

So this hadn't been Dave's first SOS.

Tears welled up in Stella's eyes. "No," she argued. "No. We have room now—we could take them in. It would probably be good to have some new people to brainstorm with. We can't just let them die of the heat like that."

"They have their Pills," he said softly. "They can take them."

Stella's mind went to her cousins, her grandparents, everyone she'd ever known who'd had to take their Pills. She shook her head. These weren't Dave's words, they were his father's.

But Dave had been the one to say them.

She'd had enough. She turned and walked out of the radio room without looking back.

Dave left her alone for a week. Then he knocked on her door. "I desire you in friendship, and I will one way or other make you amends," he said, then he paused. "That's Shakespeare."

"You read Shakespeare?"

"Cover to cover." He held up the book from the library. "Even the sonnets."

"And?"

"Not as suspenseful as a well-written molecular biology text, sure, but I liked it."

He was smiling as he said it, but the smile dropped away as Stella lifted her hand to his cheek. He stood perfectly still when she took a step forward, elevated to her tiptoes, and kissed him softly on the lips. His eyes closed and he leaned into her, almost melted into her, closing the gap between them. Then his arms wrapped tightly around her and he was kissing her back, kissing her as if it was the only thing he had ever wanted in his entire life.

"Hand me that spool of wire, will you?" Worry made Dave's voice foggy, or maybe the heat was making it difficult to hear.

"Yeah, sure." Stella figured she might as well try to be helpful, especially since she wasn't supposed to be there in the first place. She should be in class, patching together worn work clothes. The problem with patching was that it was too easy for people like Carla to run their mouths while doing it.

Stella had left at the water break, and apparently Mr. Walters had been too busy trying to deal with the rising temperature to bother sending someone out to find her.

It had taken Stella all of about a minute to locate Dave. He'd been working as a fan monitor since he turned eighteen, and there were only five stations still open. It was a real job, not like the busywork they had them doing at school, all the while pretending like they were productive citizens.

Stella brought the wire over, checking the thermometer as she did... 114° F. Six degrees higher than it was supposed to be. "Are you going to be able to fix it?"

Dave shook his head in frustration. "I'm not sure. I know Jeff would have been able to, but he created the whole damn system. They should have had him start training someone sooner—before he started losing it. His notes are a mess, especially toward the end."

By the time Stella and her dad had been placed in the high security wing, Jeff had been there for months. He'd had an unusually deep voice, and his screams had stood out, right up until the day they'd stopped completely.

Dave glanced over at her, almost as if he could guess what she was thinking. The wrench he'd been holding slipped from his grasp. He swore under his breath as it hit the ground near his feet.

Stella knelt to help him find it, the task complicated by the dim lighting and her own sweaty fingers. No wonder Dave couldn't hang onto the tools.

"Some say the world will end in fire, some say in ice. From what I've tasted of desire I hold with those who favor fire," she began reciting, under her breath.

Dave stood, wrench in hand. "Shakespeare?"

"No," Stella said. "Robert Frost. Fitting though, isn't it? I haven't been able to get it out of my head."

"I don't know," he said, his attention back on the fan. "Heat's not the same as actual fire."

Four years ago, Stella may have argued the distinction. Now, she only shrugged. "True enough, I guess. The poem's called 'Fire and Ice.' That's where Grams got the name for her book."

A minute later, Dave finished up. He stood back, listening to the humming noise, then nodded. "It's the best I can do. We may still need to seal off some more rooms eventually, but it should be okay for now."

Stella looked at the thermometer. Down to 113° F. She let out a breath she hadn't realized she'd been holding.

"So. Your grandma's book," Dave said. "Tell me what it's about."

"You never read it? You don't know the story?"

"No," he said, but his voice wavered. He was either lying, or had a particular reason for asking.

He knew. Maybe they all knew.

She fought to keep her voice light as she continued. "Well, I probably shouldn't know what it's about either. I wasn't supposed to have read it, but Grams kept leaving copies out where I could find them. It used to make my mom crazy. She and my dad thought I was too young, that it would scare me."

"And did it?"

"Oh, absolutely. But that's why I can remember it now. And the terrifying thing is that it's this, really." Stella gestured to the fan unit and the warren of rooms beyond. "Grams wrote about the bunker. She wasn't a scientist, it was all just something she imagined after reading a report in 2013 predicting the date the world would be too hot to live in, but somehow, she came up with all of this.

"There was a love story part, too," she continued, blushing a little. "That took up a lot of it, and people used to tell her how much they liked her romance novel. She'd get so mad about it—that romance was what they got out of it. She'd correct people, tell them it wasn't a romance, but a cautionary tale. I think she truly believed she could change things—that people would read this story about a girl and her boyfriend in a bunker in the not-so-distant future and start to take the warming seriously. It was her biggest disappointment—that the book sold so incredibly well, but no one changed a damn thing."

"So what happens?"

"Well, their bunker started to run out of food, and eventually the girl placed an SOS call. Not through an underground radio system, like we have here, but using some other kind of communication technology. I forget what she called it." Stella looked hard at Dave. "In the book, the fan units weren't the problem, it was the food instead, but other things were the same. Like the fact that they were afraid of contacting other bunkers.

"So the girl took things into her own hands. She

happened to find a book in their library on how to work the communication technology and taught herself. She broke into the communication room one night and sent the SOS."

"Did she tell her boyfriend what she had planned?"

Stella shook her head. Heart pounding, she asked, "Do you think what she did was right?"

"Depends on how the book ends."

Stella frowned. That was the difference between the two of them. Dave thought right and wrong depended on outcome. Stella believed they simply were.

"Did you know that Grams was the one to pick the books for our library?" she asked, switching tactics.

"I didn't," he said, looking at her warily.

Surely he'd figured it out.

But she pressed forward anyway. "She included a book on how to work an underground radio system."

He nodded thoughtfully. "Of course she did."

Someone began playing the piano, sounds of a Hummel Sonata drifting down the hallway. Her father, maybe? It was near impossible to say. In four years, with little else to do, most of them had become proficient.

Stella watched the thermometer rise again to 114° F. She couldn't bring herself to point it out to Dave. He wasn't looking at it, or even at her, staring instead through the corridor into the main entry room. Staring at the metal door to the outside world.

"How did it end?" he asked abruptly.

"What?" A rhythmic pounding, the beat all wrong for the sonata, distracted her. She heard the pianist falter, then recover and continue louder, as if determined to drown out the noise.

"How did the book end? Did they make it? The girl and

her boyfriend?" His voice was still quiet, but insistent.

The pounding persisted, until at last Stella found herself turning and following Dave's eyes to the metal door. It had begun to shake.

She grabbed his hand. She shouldn't be scared. This was what she had wanted, after all.

No, not what she wanted, not what anyone wanted, but at least this way they'd have a chance.

She turned to Dave, wishing she could lie and say that Grams' book gave them their happily ever after.

But the door had begun to collapse inward, and all she could tell him was the truth.

"Like this," she forced herself to say, her attention never leaving the door. "Her book ended with the door opening. Exactly like this."

THE LOVE RIDDLE

Gail Oare

It doesn't ask
　It tells
It defies physical law
　Existing everywhere all at once
It's not measureable
　But abundant
It's both visible and invisible
　And we see both

It holds groups together
　Even when apart
People of all faiths and those without
　Believe in it
It grows stronger with age
　Stronger when tested
It laughs and cries
　It rebirths itself

It comes in many forms
    And continues to find new shapes
Like crystal stars in a merlot sky
    It is mysterious and eternal
It fills a life
    And fills the world
And all it covers
    Is for the better
It is indefinable
    But in loving we define it.

RED SKY

Abigail Drake

Seeing the ghost of my dead little sister before I'd even had my morning coffee never boded well. I rubbed my face with my hands, hoping to erase the vision, but she remained. Small. Blonde. Perfect. And forever eight years old.

She stood next to me on the front stoop of my house, right next to a pot of brightly colored fall mums. She'd always loved fall. A smile played on the corners of her lips as she traced a finger over the burgundy blossoms.

"Why are you here, Lucy?"

"I think you know, Maggie," she answered in a singsong voice. Her eyes, as blue as the sky on a cloudless summer day, were focused on the horizon as if she could see the sun about to rise. "Red sky at night, sailor's delight. Red sky at morning, sailors take warning."

"Oh, great. Again with the cryptic warnings? It's bad enough you're haunting me, please don't torture me, too."

"I'm not torturing you."

"What are you trying to tell me, kiddo?" I kneeled next to her, my gaze skimming over her golden hair, and the deep dimple playing hide-and-seek on her sweetly rounded cheek. She'd never lost her baby fat. She hadn't lived long enough.

"I'm not trying to tell you anything," she said, her gaze still on the eastern horizon, her voice completely devoid of emotion. "I'm trying to warn you, because it's the only way I can help. Don't you understand?"

"No, I don't understand. You keep showing up here, telling me something bad is about to happen, but you never give any details. Details would be helpful."

She shrugged. "You always figure it out. You found Mrs. Hammerstein in her basement, didn't you?"

"I got lucky."

"No such thing as luck, Mags. We both know that much."

At her words, the old wound deep inside me throbbed, the same way it had every day for nearly two decades. I reached out to touch her, but before my hand could make contact with her skin, she disappeared, like fog evaporating in the morning light. I sighed, sitting down on the damp cement of my front step and inhaling the spicy fragrance of the mums. The cold entered my body through my thin running pants, but I didn't get up. I stayed in that position as a burst of bright fuchsia color stained the sky and the sun slowly began its ascent.

Red sky at morning, sailors take warning.

I had problems. Serious problems. Normal people did not interact with ghosts on a regular basis. I'd tried everything I could think of, including therapy, but nothing helped. My therapist called her a manifestation of my grief. Nice to know, but useless, since nothing I did made Lucy's ghost go away. Not therapy. Not an exorcism. Not burning sage or blessed amulets. Definitely not a Ouija board. I'd tried that once in college, and that attempt had failed miserably. Lucy decided it would be a fun way to freak out my sorority sisters, and it worked. Two girls quit school and I got kicked out of the Theta house.

Thanks, Lucy.

It had gotten worse since I moved back home after a brief period living in the city. Lucy didn't like me living in the city. She wanted me to come back to our little town on the banks of the Ohio River, and I did as she requested. Unfortunately, now, instead of just appearing in front of me and freaking me out—something Lucy seemed to enjoy immensely—she'd become the voice of doom.

The day I found Mrs. Hammerstein, Lucy had shown up as I was gardening. She stood in the corner of my yard, saying, "Jack fell down and broke his crown," over and over again. When she turned and began skipping down the street, I'd followed her, right to Mrs. Hammerstein's house. The poor old lady had taken a tumble down her basement stairs. She hadn't broken her crown, but she had broken a hip, and would have died if I hadn't found her when I did.

Then there was the day I'd been on an important conference call for work. Lucy appeared next to me, screaming, "And down will come baby, cradle and all," at the top of her voice, eyes wide with panic. I'd known immediately which baby she referred to, since my next-door neighbor Aimee had given birth only a few weeks ago, and she and Lucy had been classmates and good friends. I knew my sister checked in on her from time to time. To my horror, I found Aimee standing on her roof in her nightgown, her baby clutched in her arms. I reached her just in time.

All in all, this was the eighth time my sister had shown up reciting some creepy nursery rhyme and expecting me to somehow figure out what she wanted me to do, who she wanted me to save. Nearly twenty years had passed since Lucy died, but I still couldn't seem to move on with my life. She wouldn't let me.

My parents had forgiven me long ago. They blamed themselves for allowing a teenager to watch an eight year old on the crowded shores of a lake. They'd gotten divorced two years later. Grief had eventually made them hate each other, but not me. They never hated me. It made me feel even worse, because I knew the truth. I was the one to blame.

"Are you going to sit there all day or are we going to run?" asked my best friend, Christie, taking me out of my reverie. Her pale hair was pulled into a tight ponytail, and she jogged in place as she waited for me. I joined her, the cold moisture from the step still clinging to my skin.

We ran slowly through the town, down empty tree-lined streets and past rows of elegant Victorian houses with perfectly manicured lawns. My thoughts were still on Lucy, but soon the rhythmic sound of our feet hitting the pavement calmed me.

People were just beginning to wake up, and several called out a greeting to us as we passed. We'd become fixtures in this place, as regular as clockwork. Christie and I had lived here our whole lives, except for my brief attempt to live in the city right after college, and her short stint in the military. We were known here, and as much a part of the fabric of this town as the river that ran along its border. We couldn't escape it, and, at this point, we really didn't want to. We'd both come back for a reason. Christie came to marry her high school sweetheart, Tom, and care for her aging mother. I came because my dead sister demanded it. Unfortunately, Lucy wasn't the only ghost from my past in this town.

"Have you seen Joe lately?" asked Christie, panting slightly. "Tom said he's been asking about you."

I nearly tripped on a tree root poking out of the sidewalk. "Asking about me how?"

Joe and I had dated throughout high school and college. He'd been with me the day Lucy died. But I'd never been able to tell him about her visits. I didn't want him to think I was crazy and leave me. Instead, the weight of keeping such a secret had become too much, and I'd left him. He'd moved back to town a few months ago and was now our police chief. Every time I saw him in his blue uniform, I felt a stab of pain, but I knew I'd done the right thing. I didn't deserve to have nice things.

Christie shot me a look out of the corner of her eye. "He's worried about you. We all are. Even your mom and dad—"

I waved away her words. "I'm fine."

"You're not fine, Maggie."

Shrugging, I answered her honestly. I hid very little from my oldest friend. "I'm as fine as I can be, and that's enough, okay?"

"Okay," she said, but I could tell she was not convinced.

We stopped, as we always did, at the bakery for coffee and a donut, completely negating the efforts of our run. As we walked back home, warm coffees clutched in our hands and the sugary taste of the donuts still on our tongues, we saw Nutsy Bob out walking his dog, Miss Clementine.

Nutsy Bob. Another fixture in our town, we'd known him since we were small. Something bad had happened to him during the war, making him not quite right in the head, but he was harmless and sweet. Miss Clementine, on the other hand, was a monster. A nasty little Yorkie, she liked to chomp on ankles, especially mine, whenever she had a chance.

Nutsy greeted us as he always did. "Howdy do, howdy do," he said, a giant smile plastered on his face and a completely vacant look in his eyes. His dark hair was slicked back and his black, horn-rimmed glasses spanned a distance wider than his face. He wore a plaid shirt, impeccably ironed, as always, and jeans that had been ironed as well with a perfectly straight crease down the front. I looked down at my wrinkled and stained t-shirt. I hadn't come close to ironing anything in years. The advantage of working from home.

"Hi, Bob." I narrowed my eyes at his canine companion. "Hello, hell hound."

Miss Clementine snarled, moving into attack mode, and I jumped away, nearly tripping on her leash. I heard Christie smother a giggle and I glared at her as Nutsy Bob reached down to soothe the irate little dog.

"It's okay, Miss Clementine," he murmured as the vicious demon dog licked his hand lovingly. "She didn't mean it. Did you, Maggie?"

"No. I didn't mean it. I'm sorry." I took a step forward, hoping to make peace with Miss Clementine, but she growled, showing me her razor sharp, mutant teeth. I backed off. I didn't have time to deal with puncture wounds this morning.

"That dog really hates you," said Christie, taking a sip of her coffee as we walked away. She enjoyed this way too much. Miss Clementine never growled at Christie. Maybe the little dog sensed Lucy's presence around me. Or maybe Miss Clementine was just a jerk. It could go either way.

"The feeling is mutual, trust me," I said. "She almost got my ankle this time. Maybe that was what this morning's warning was about."

"What warning?" asked Christie.

"Nothing." I felt my cheeks get hot. Christie stopped in her tracks, her eyes huge in her face.

"It was Lucy again, wasn't it?" When I didn't reply, she groaned. "Maggie, you have to start taking this seriously. You need to talk to someone."

"If I tell anyone, they'll think I'm crazy," I said, "and they would probably be right."

"You aren't crazy, Maggie." Christie put a comforting hand on my arm. "We have to figure this out. Every time she has come to you, it's been for a reason."

"I know." I threw my empty coffee cup into a garbage can, picturing Lucy's face from this morning, her sweet forever childish face. "But it's not really about me. Not anymore at least. This is the eighth time she's done this, but she only comes to me now in order to help someone else."

"Or maybe that's not it at all."

"What do you mean?"

She put a hand on my arm. "This is the eighth time, right? Lucy lived eight years. Could it be that she's helping you find a way to forgive yourself and move on? Like a kind of penance?"

"So you're saying my dead eight-year-old sister created this whole cosmic web of intrigue as a way to help me forgive myself?"

Christie bit her lip. "I'm just saying it's possible. It started when you moved back here, right after you broke up with Joe."

I rolled my eyes. "Joe has nothing to do with this."

"Maybe, and maybe not." Christie had a look in her eye that meant she was on the verge of solving something, some kind of puzzle. I knew that look well. "But there is a reason why this is happening right now. I think Lucy is trying to help you."

I let out a harsh laugh. "I doubt it."

Christie didn't say anything. She knew how I felt. Two minutes of distraction and selfishness had cost the life of my sister and destroyed my family as well.

Compounding my guilt? The last words I'd said to Lucy were to tell her to stop bugging me so that I could hang out with my friends. I was thirteen and an idiot. I didn't pay attention to her, and didn't notice when she waded into the lake, leaving her little pink bucket in the sand. Because of me, she'd died, and part of me had died that day, too.

I walked Christie to her house, trying to ignore the look of concern on her face as I waved goodbye. Shoving my hands in the pockets of my jacket, I walked aimlessly, not realizing where my feet were taking me until I reached the banks of the river. I sank down onto a wooden bench and watched the dark, muddy water flow past me. The river, swollen because of recent rain, looked powerful and threatening. Usually this was my favorite place to relax, but somehow the force and speed of the water made me anxious and unsettled. I got up to leave, just as a cloud covered the sun and the morning suddenly felt like the edge of night.

Could Christie be right? Could this be the last time? Was this Lucy trying to find a way to help me finally get over what happened so many years ago? If helping eight people meant our debt would be paid, I'd be willing to accept it. The more I considered it, the more this felt like a final act of love from my sister.

But who did I have to save in order to save myself?

I shivered, a prickly sensation on the back of my neck. I tried to ignore it. There was no sign of Lucy anywhere, but the weather had changed dramatically, and it looked like it was about to rain. Sensible people were safe inside their houses, not out wandering next to dangerously high rivers. I shook my head, getting annoyed with myself, and decided to be sensible as well. I took one last glance at the river as I left, and that was when I saw it.

Something was in the river. At first I thought it was a log, but then I realized it was a person, clinging to a fallen tree in the water and waving feebly. I ran down to the side of the river, sliding in the mud and on the slick grass, and saw Nutsy Bob, holding Miss Clementine and trying to keep her head above water. She looked like a bedraggled rat and he didn't look much better. I could tell he didn't have much time. His face was pale and gray, and he seemed to be losing his grip.

I dug into my pocket for my cell phone, calling for help as I grabbed a long tree branch that had washed ashore and waded into the river as far as I dared. The cold water pounded against my legs, and the thick mud pulled at my shoes, making each step difficult. After a few terrifying moments, I got the branch out far enough that Nutsy could reach it, but he was too weak to hold on. I forced myself deeper into the water, ignoring the bite of the cold as it seemed to clench my bones in its icy jaws.

"Give me the dog so that you can hold on," I said through chattering teeth. It was fall, but the weather had been remarkably cold this year and the water was frigid.

Nutsy Bob shook his head. "I can't. I won't let her go."

His eyes were beginning to glaze over, and I knew I didn't have much time. My feet were now stuck in the mud of the riverbed. I experienced a moment of panic when I couldn't pull my feet free, but I gave another tug and felt my running shoes slide off. Without my shoes on it was easier to reach him. I grabbed him by the collar of his jacket and pulled him slowly to shore. It was only a few yards, but it felt like miles. Miss Clementine, shivering in his arms, growled at me halfheartedly as the skies opened and it began to rain.

The ambulance and firemen arrived moments later and put Nutsy on a stretcher. "He must have slipped off the path and fallen in," said one of the paramedics, wrapping a blanket around my shoulders as he pointed to tracks in the mud near where I'd found Nutsy. "It's a good thing you were here."

I lifted my face to the sky, letting the cool rain wash away the dirty water of the river. My legs were covered in mud up to my knees, and I had lost my brand-new running shoes to the power of the river, but I was feeling remarkably unscathed. I looked up the hill and saw the lights of a police car. I swallowed hard as a tall and very familiar figure in blue began heading my way.

Joe knelt beside me, pulling the blanket tightly around my shoulders. "You again, Maggie?"

The rain dripped off his hat and onto the shoulders of his uniform, but he seemed oblivious. He stared at me, his dark eyes worried as he scanned my face. I'd fallen in love with those eyes a long time ago, but years of hurt and misunderstanding had created a chasm between us as wide as the river.

"What happened?" he asked.

"I was running with Christie, and I felt like taking a walk afterward."

He gave me a crooked smile, the kind that always did funny things to my stomach and had gotten me into trouble more than once in high school. "You mean after you stopped for a donut and coffee?"

I nodded. "Are we that predictable?"

"Sometimes."

A muscle worked in his jaw as he glanced away, but the hurt I'd seen in his expression was almost too much to bear. I looked at my hands clutching the edge of the blanket. They were white and my fingertips seemed to be tinged with blue. I curled them into tight little fists, trying to make them feel warm again.

He sighed, scratching his jaw. "I can't decide if you are always at the right place at the right time or the wrong place at the wrong time. Which one is it, Mags?"

He reverted into his old pet name for me as easily as slipping into a worn out and comfortable pair of jeans. I shrugged. "I don't know, either."

He took my cold hands in his and began rubbing them. It felt so good I closed my eyes and sighed.

"You can't keep doing this. If you keep saving people and jumping into rivers all the time, the rest of us are going to be out of a job."

I giggled because I couldn't help it, but then I thought of Lucy's ghostly face and shivered. Her visits were becoming more and more frequent, and I was getting worried.

Joe wrapped an arm around my shoulders and helped me to my feet. My white socks were now caked with brown heavy mud and soaking wet, and my hair had slipped out of its ponytail and stuck to my cheeks in long, black strands. Joe brushed my hair out of my face and helped me up the hill.

Nutsy lay on a stretcher, covered in blankets, with his tiny dog by his side. Nutsy was barely conscious, but he still cradled her gently in his arms. He wouldn't let go of her. He couldn't. Miss Clementine growled as soon as she saw me.

"Ungrateful little rat," I muttered, and Joe laughed.

Nutsy mumbled something through chattering teeth, repeating what sounded like a mantra. I leaned down to hear him, ignoring the fact that Miss Clementine was now nearly vibrating with anger. His words made my heart stop in my chest.

"Red sky at morning, sailors take warning," he said, over and over again as they wheeled him slowly away.

EBBY & OSCAR

Kathleen Shoop

Ebby Stewart drew a deep breath and entered Harvest Moon Foods. Scented waves of roses, heliotrope, lavender, hyacinth, and gardenias swept her, as though selected as part of a campaign to cheer her up. Eight-thirty, ten miles run, mind clear. The store was part fancy fruits, part bargain produce, part upscale gift shop—the perfect metaphor for Eagle Bend, Pennsylvania.

She yanked wipes from the dispenser and used half to clean the cart handle and the others to mop the back of her neck and hands. Picking through the greenest Granny Smiths, the sound of guitar strumming drew her attention. In the café area the singer du jour belted out "Danny's Song," the greatest, saddest, leaving-the-bar-in-tears song ever. The vocalist delivered the exact resentful venom Ebby embodied and so she harmonized, tossing apples into a net bag before moving to the melons.

"Hey, Eb."

Ebby cringed and clutched a watermelon to her belly. Ebby wasn't in the mood to face her. Not that day.

"Hi."

Sue Wilde Carson looked Ebby up and down, judging, same as always.

Ebby bit her lip, sharply aware of her sweat-drenched tank and running shorts. The bun had been messy even before her run and now must have shifted to rat's nest status.

"Hmm." Ebby returned Sue's assessing look. Perfection as usual. Blonde "passport hair" and light makeup camouflaged any hint of exhaustion that having a ton of kids should have brought. Sue's tan shoulders and legs glistened while her Amelia Pettipiece sleeveless shift in white eyelet with Tori Burch flipflops conveyed everything Ebby had thought she'd be but wasn't by the time she turned thirty-two.

Sue's platoon bellowed hellos to Aunt Ebby, yanking on her with sticky paws.

"They know I'm not their aunt, right?"

"Basically you are."

Ebby shrugged. Basically not. She tried to track the kids as they darted in between the fruit and veggie stands. The oldest boy and girl commandeered a cucumber and a plum to use as a bat and ball. Swing and a hit, the plum whizzed toward Ebby. Her hand darted out to snatch the fruit before it pelted the old man behind her. The other five children, yes seven all together, fell out on separate missions, swarming various produce zones filling bags with groceries of their choice.

Ebby blew out her air, conscious she was scowling. "Isn't it time you stopped dressing them like quints plus two?" She wiggled her forefinger at several as they swerved in between the two women, one of them crawling through Ebby's legs.

The acoustic guitar player sang louder, even more raw. Ebby shook her head. She would do the rest of her shopping and loop back to the produce after the Carsons had cleared out.

Sue followed Ebby. "Anthony said the same thing the other day."

The sound of Ebby's ex-husband's name bristled her. One of the heathens smacked Ebby in the back of her feet with their cart. "Ouch, jeeze."

Sue scooped up the offender and plunked her onto her hip, brushing some dirt from her cheek. "She didn't mean it, Eb."

Ebby stopped in front of the singer as Sue's kids tossed fruits and nuts and crackers into her cart. She tried to stop them but the man strummed louder, sparks flying from his fingertips, masking her protestations.

"Lighten up, Eb. It's time. My brother told me—"

Ebby snapped toward Sue. Her rival might have been correct but she had a right to her anger. This time of year was the worst. Ebby reached for a carrot bundle, the long greens on the ends swaying as she pointed it at Sue. "You stole my husband."

"Anthony came to me. Ten years... after you and he—"

Ebby jammed the carrots into the seat where a child should sit. It wasn't as though she wanted Anthony. It was the point of the thievery. She had to get out of there. She shoved her cart forward, but the wheel jammed and it slammed into the pineapple bin, knocking several off. The tornado of children dizzied her, panicked breathing threatening. Damn therapy. Her past was more prominent than ever. Instead of releasing like the "healer" had advertised, the torment swelled her insides, billowed around her then jelled on her skin.

Another heave of the cart and it smacked the fruit bin, knocking the whole thing over. The kids squealed as crowned fruits rolled around. Finally the wheels unjammed and Ebby sped away.

Looking back, Sue extended her hands, palms up, folding her fingers up and down. "Come, come, children." And like Snow White calling her squirrels and birds and dwarves, half the children collapsed around her, helping to clean up the mess Ebby had made. The other half followed Ebby, putting all manner of unwanted things into her cart.

Oscar Wilde, named for the writer, was tall and lanky, sunburned and smiling when Ebby rolled up to his checkout line. She'd considered going to another cashier. But that wouldn't help. He knew where to find her. He knew what date it was.

She grabbed a water from the cooler and drank half while placing items onto the belt. She gestured with the bottle. "Not the stapler."

Oscar set it in the go-back cart.

"Not the loofah. Uh, wait. Not the pink one. Yes to the blue one."

Oscar lifted his eyebrows following directions.

"No to the Kleenex. Yes to the paper towels."

He sighed and tossed them to his bagger, Leo.

When she'd finished unloading, she stood in front of the screen where she punched in her loyalty card info. She could feel Oscar's smile. She added her phone number. "Your sister's rugrats tailed me all over the store. I'm in a mood."

"I heard."

She looked at him. "She couldn't wait to report."

He keyed in some info on his side. "You know it's time. Right?"

She eyed him then went back to plugging her zip-code into the monitor.

He leaned on the edge of the belt. "It's my job, isn't it? That's why you won't just follow your heart right to me."

She scoffed.

"Just so you know, my wrought iron business is rocketing."

She shook her head.

"Come on."

She sighed. "You're a walking, talking Hallmark movie hero. I hardly think you need to scrounge a date up with me."

He smiled, satisfied-looking. "You're a mess."

"Don't compare my outsides to your insides, fella."

"That's some real good recovering alcoholic talk."

"You would know."

"So, tonight then." He wiped down the conveyor belt.

Leo turned his attention back and forth between the two. "You did promise, Ebby. Last week. Right here in our checkout lane."

She pushed her debit card into the reader. "Isn't that a nice set of satellite ears you've got, Leo?" Ebby couldn't shoulder another failure.

"I'll bring food. Your place," Oscar said. "I've got something for you."

She was weakening. Wanting to let Oscar over the threshold of her heart brought anxiety, excitement, and her barbwired mood.

"Tomorrow," she said. "I'll make something."

Oscar scanned her grocery haul. "Fruit salad?"

"I should have gone in Maryellen Robuck's lane."

"You'd be here till midnight."

"You're nosy. Both of you," she said.

"Yes," Oscar said.

A grin swallowed his face, making her soften even more. "Don't get comfy with anything."

Leo handed off her full cart.

"Thank you." She pushed it toward the door. "Your sister and her insane kid posse screwed up my morning."

He smiled broader.

As she approached the exit she looked over her shoulder and heard Leo say, "You guys are drunks? AA? Seriously?"

Ebby felt a flutter deep in her belly as she caught Oscar watching her. A gush of thick, humid air burned her skin. And for a moment she thought something could actually be different. After years of turmoil, maybe she was ready for Oscar. The world was full of miracles. Why couldn't she have one for herself?

Summer solstice. Divorce, sorrow, joy, love, heartbreak, loss, breakups, sex, love, hate, utter failure of various sorts, death. Three deaths. She finished making the tomato, swiss and mayo sandwiches, put them in the fridge, plumped the couch pillows, fluffed her hair, and padded to the door when Oscar knocked.

She flung it open. His blond hair, neatly combed back, still wet after a shower, and steady blue-eyed gaze released the flutters that had started the day before. Frightened again, she nearly pushed him back out, but he'd already strode past her to the back deck overlooking the Allegheny River.

"God, gorgeous."

"View's worth every cent."

He turned. "I meant you."

She couldn't talk so she pressed her belly to keep from melting into his arms. "I was a mess when you saw me yesterday. Nothing's changed."

"I know." He handed her two wrapped gifts.

She bounced them up and down, feeling their weight. "Grocery bag wrapping. Ingenious."

"Start with the heavy one."

She set them down on the coffee table and pulled embroidery scissors from a basket. She slid on her glasses and plopped on the couch next to Oscar.

"Nice spectacles."

"Can't believe I need readers. Turned thirty-two and suddenly I can't read my manuscripts."

"Cat eyes. Retro."

"Nope. Real thing. Got 'em at Miller's Antiques and my doc did 'em up with new lenses."

"You make me smile."

They were avoiding the subject. "Franklin hated them."

"Franklin's a dolt."

She looked over the readers at Oscar. "Isn't he? Do you know he broke up with me because—"

"Wait," Oscar held up a finger. "Mrs. Terry told me a month ago."

She cocked her head. "Go on."

"Oh my God, you're sexy." He slid closer, his body warming her.

"What'd you hear?" Ebby poked the sharp embroidery scissors into one fingertip, then the next and next.

"That Franklin overheard you on a call and—"

"Don't look at me like that. A girl's got to eat. My romance readers love these Zoom readings. I don't know what to say."

"It's your job. I love that it's your job."

His sly smile made her roll her eyes. "Oh, man. You men."

"So, while Mrs. Terry was stocking up on Hanes extra, extra-large underwear, she said that Franklin told his mother who told Mari Holmes that you were using your sex life in your novels."

He drew a circle on her knee.

Franklin told his mother? Ebby blew out her air. She'd gotten out of the relationship in the nick of time. "That's not right."

He lifted his eyebrows.

"Well, partially. I was using the relationship in my books. But not salaciously. It was for the parts that were boring. You know how the stories go—main character's life is falling apart, she's had it with run-of-the-mill missionary and inattentive boyfriend and she breaks loose and finally finds her soulmate. Readers love when she finds the right man and nothing's boring anymore, not even the ordinary stuff."

"You hit the *USAToday* bestseller list with the last one, right?"

She doffed her scissors at him. "*Love in the Time of Heartbreak.* He didn't like being experimental data for my work."

"You really didn't love him."

"Hell no. And it wasn't my using our boring sex as fodder that sent him packing."

Oscar furrowed his brow.

"It was you."

Oscar pulled a face. "Oh, wow."

"Our endless phone calls and coffees."

Oscar ran his hand through his hair. "He knew we were friends forever. I never... oh... that day I called... oh... That makes sense. But it wasn't as though we were discussing the temperature at which iron is malleable."

"Not every time." She winked. "I had you on speaker right before he broke up with me. He thought all that hot iron talk was a metaphor for us getting hot and bothered and... that was the final straw."

"Poor guy."

"I warned him."

"He'll be fine."

"Totally. He's got his pick of five debutantes for the club picnic."

Oscar set one present on her lap. *Snip, snip, snip.* She surgically clipped at the raffia and wrapping.

She lifted the object. A wrought iron number 8. She ran her fingers around it, tears gathering.

He removed her glasses and wiped her wet cheeks with his thumbs. "I was hoping you'd love it."

"I do. Eight years sober."

"I had to give you something permanent. It'll last ten lifetimes unless it falls into the bowels of hell or..." He turned it sideways. "It's infinity, too. Forever. And see here... for your parents—I melded on a replica of your house and here this little foot for..."

Tears continued to fall. She couldn't stop the emotion from emptying out. He brushed her hair behind her ear and she caught his wrist and latched onto it. She couldn't breathe even as her heart raced. They leaned into each other and kissed.

She was struck by the sense of home, belonging, entering a familiar world. Why had she resisted for so long? Like magic, she'd gone home. He pulled her onto his lap, they kissed and caressed and found each other yet again. If someone had seen them in profile, infinity signs could have been traced around their entwined limbs... them, their togetherness filling her, making her whole. And she exhaled for the first time in ages.

Sometime during the night, the sound of boaters laughing and singing offkey Vance Joy wakened Oscar. Moonlight spilled through the doors from the deck, glinting off the iron 8. "Open the second one," he said.

She eyed the package but didn't reach for it. It was the present, despite its lightness, that carried all the weight. She put her t-shirt and shorts back on and went to the deck. The wind lifted her long brown hair, twirling it as though the gusts had fingers, exposing her graceful neck. He pulled on his shorts, his nerves tangling. He had to do it. He'd promised her he'd remember.

And so he handed her the light, soft package. She drew a deep breath and slipped the ribbon off. He knew every thought that ricocheted through her mind. Eight years of close, raw, recovery friendship did that. She slid her finger under the tape and lifted the flap. Under the sapphire blue sky, the boat music playing, she lifted the small blanket from the packaging and held it against her chest, then to her nose, trying to inhale her past, the life that slipped away and turned it all wrong for her. He pulled her close. She stiffened.

"You have to go," she said.

"Eb, please."

"This was nice. You cleansed my sexual palate and there's no one I'd rather have do that than you because..."

"No. I won't let you do this."

"Do what? I'll hurt you again and again and you'll never move on."

"You can't hurt me if I stay. I know all your faults. Something will always make you run a little bit away," he said. "I understand you lost your baby, your husband, your parents. I understand that you hate cooking but love baking, you hoard things you don't need, you put the toilet paper on the holder willy-nilly, you hate showers but love standing in the rain, you hate my sister for stealing Anthony but not really... not anymore. And even though it breaks your heart every time you run into her and her twenty kids, you send every single one of them a present on their birthdays and—"

She stormed away. "Stop."

He followed. "I know that loss has turned you selfish and small and you have carved out this island of existence with nothing but a single palm tree so you easily dodge falling coconuts and you can't make missteps and hurt anymore and all you're left with is the familiar pain that you can numb out of and... you told me to give you that blanket back at eight years. You told me then you'd be ready. I'm not asking you to change a single thing about yourself."

She swallowed hard and backed away. "You're so incredibly kind and loving and talented and... You deserve someone who's all those things too."

He shook his head. "You have to trust me. It wasn't your fault."

She kept backing away, the blanket tight against her chest, the pale blue fleece bordered with shiny, navy silk that bore spots where her little boy had begun to wear it thin. She caressed the trim and it was as though Oscar could see her holding the child she used to bundle in it. He wondered for the first time if she'd ever be able to love him back. He would have sworn in court that she did, that they were soul-tied, forever bound by something he couldn't even name. His throat thickened, keeping him from feeling anything but crushing fear.

"You could get used to happiness, to being with me the same way you've gotten used to pain and being alone. We could start a family tomorrow."

She looked away. For a moment he thought those few words were all it took for her to embrace what she'd been fighting all along.

Her silence deafened him. Minutes passed. "Okay then," he said.

She met his gaze, leaving sad hardness like an iron ingot on his chest.

"Okay then." She disappeared into the bedroom, the door clicking shut, the boaters singing Meatloaf's "Two Out of Three Ain't Bad" so loud he thought they'd been narrating just for them.

Ebby had shopped at Giant Eagle in Wolf's Run for two weeks, avoiding Oscar, his sister, everyone. But then she heard that Oscar had quit when an enormous commission to create railings, doors, and entryways for a custom builder turned his hobby into a full-time job.

She entered Harvest Moon, the guitar player already elbow-deep in Bonnie Tyler's "It's a Heartache." The primal rendition pulled a thread in her and she turned to leave.

"Eb."

God... Her. Again.

"Sue."

"You saved me a trip."

Ebby lifted her shoulders, confused.

Sue approached with the youngest baby. Auberly was her name... maybe. She handed the child to Ebby.

Ebby pushed her back. "Um... what the hell?"

Sue handed Ebby some car keys. "Car seat's in the van. Diaper bag, everything."

"Are you crazy?"

Sue shrugged. "Okay. Which other kid then?"

The baby started to fuss, kicking her legs. Ebby held her close, shushing her as Sue practically ran away.

"Where the hell are you going?" Ebby followed her.

Sue said over her shoulder, "I'll get her Monday."

"You can't just drop a kid off like a sack of sugar. I oughta call the cops."

"I trust you." She waved over her head.

"Trust me?"

Sue stopped. "Stop blaming yourself. Anthony was there too. SIDS is not someone's fault. These seven kids ought to prove that." Two of the other kids latched onto her legs.

Ebby's mind twisted, squeezing her heart, the truth oozing inside her. The therapist had been trying to get her to vocalize the night's events. Suddenly the words poured out. "We were both there but I was tired of Anthony working and not helping and I just wanted him to get the baby. Just once to feed him. So when Max cried, I didn't respond because it was Anthony's turn and then just that silence..."

Sue moved closer. "It's pure luck that any of these kids are alive. I'm sure I don't watch them anywhere near how close you watched Max."

Ebby looked away.

"If taking your eye off someone—a baby, a boyfriend, a friend was all it took for the person to disappear, then my brother would be long gone from your life."

"A good mother would have known. Would have felt something was wrong and gone to him no matter what."

"I trust you. Oscar trusts you," Sue said. "And it's time for you to trust Oscar."

Ebby's knees went weak. Strong arms caught her from behind. The scent of wood soap and grease filled her nose. *Oscar.*

He stepped around Ebby and took her free hand. "Please, let me love you."

Ebby looked into his eyes and the snarl of emotion that plagued her for nearly a decade began to unspool. She glanced at Sue who was smiling through tears and took the baby.

Oscar pulled Ebby closer. "If you don't want to get married," he said, "if you don't want kids, I'll be there forever. Say yes to that. And let's stop with all the phone calls and Franklins and... let me be the one who gives you boring material for your books."

Everything they'd been building was finally as solid as the iron Oscar had shaped into the infinity 8. She'd never felt a sense of happiness as strongly as she'd felt grief. Until now.

"Yes." She latched onto him so tight she couldn't inhale. He swallowed her up, his breath catching in her ear. Like heat that melted for wrought iron to take its final form, Ebby finally felt shaped. And they held each other in the grocery store, guitar woman singing, Sue and her passel of kids dashing around. Ebby finally let go of the pain and took hold of Oscar, of the love that had been there all along.

Oh, Wow!

Madhu Bazaz Wangu

Priya had a few weeks to live, the nurse holding her hand tried to tell her in a roundabout way. The other woman's eyes were wet. She did not let go until the physician arrived.

"I'm afraid, Doctor," Priya said. "So is this sweet nurse."

"Who doesn't fear death?" asked the doctor who must have witnessed patients die. Then he answered his own question. "We all do." Unlike the nurse's roundabout way, his declaration of the diagnosis was more direct. "I'm so sorry to inform you that the cancer of the uterus is at the fourth stage. You may go home now. Your husband will take good care of you. You two may want to be together in the comfort of your home at such a time."

Priya already knew how her life was to end much before the kind nurse or the nonchalant doctor announced it. She was not calm but angry—no, incensed—with no one in particular.

After the doctor and nurse left the examination room, Priya sat up on the table for half a minute, inhaling and exhaling a long sigh. Then she dressed herself, combed her hair, slipped on her sandals and gathered her purse. Deliberately she exited the room.

Priya took a shortcut down a long corridor branching into the terminal cancer area. The ward was filled with uncanny silence. Most rooms had a patient with one visitor... or none. Her pace slowed. Soon she would be one of them. A monitoring machine in the room she was passing suddenly made unusual sounds. Priya could see it through the open door. Then just as suddenly, it stopped beeping.

Priya shuffled closer to the threshold of the room. She was able to see the dying patient's face. His head looked comfortable on the soft white pillow and his face peaceful with a subtle smile playing on his lips. The only sound she could hear was him whisper, "Oh, wow!" He kept repeating the two words until their sound got dimmer and dimmer and dimmer and then disappeared.

Breaking the silence of the space, she heard someone asking her to move away. Doctors and nurses came rushing past, bustling inside the room, adjusting the monitor. But the patient was gone.

Priya advanced her steps toward the parking lot. She decided until she received definitive test results, she was not going to think about all this. But what was the man wowing? Was he having a good dream moments before he died? Somewhere she had read that when a dying person lets go of all he held onto in this life—such as his successes, possessions, positions, and most significantly the tenderness and affection for their loved ones—such a release was liberating. It would feel like lustrous joy, a sense of bliss. Priya climbed into her car and drove home.

It had been a week since her doctor's appointment at the hospital. It took much longer to make a cup of cardamom tea than it used to. The aroma of the leaves mixed with the spice and soothed her. She felt no pain and made herself comfortable on her favorite chair, then switched on the television. The meteorologist was still discussing the tsunami that had engulfed a small island about a hundred miles away from the main island where Priya lived. Kaput! Millions of years sunk in the ocean. Forever. First the enormous wind. Then fire. Then all submerged. Not a single man, woman or child was told that this natural disaster was going to suck the life out of them. Twenty-four hours of gloom and doom for an exotic holiday island, not very different than her own, was being reeled on the television over and over, as if a reality show.

Priya had nowhere to go, nothing new to do. She did what she did every evening. She tilted her rocking chair that seemed to grumble, then picked up a drawing pad and a pencil. Near a window under a standing lamp she put final touches to a colored sketch she had been working on for days. She had almost completed a scene that Manohar, her husband, liked so much that he wanted to get it framed. It depicted a bamboo gate on a path through a canopy of trees toward some unknown distant destination.

The sharp nib of her pencil was used up and blunted. She sharpened and then re-sharpened it several times more before she was done. The night got darker. Through the window she saw lightning bugs glistening over the darkened grass and against the silhouette of the hills, the trees and the rooftops in the inky night. What would she look at when she could no longer see?

She felt Manohar's kiss on the back of her head. Then his warm strong hands massaged her shoulders. "Enough of news! What would you like for dinner?"

"Surprise me! I like everything you make."

He switched off the television and switched on a recording of Ravi Shankar playing raga jog on sitar. Allah Rakkha accompanied on tabla. Sweet waves of music soothed her mind. Priya loved it when Manohar practiced playing sitar although he was not as good as Ravi Shankar… yet. At one point the pencil rose and pressed in rhythm with the movement of the strings and the beats. The sound, the composition and Priya became one. Her sketch was almost complete. She felt like resting for a few minutes. Immediately a thought floated in. *How can I tell Manohar the way I feel? How do I put in words to gently convey how the tsunami that swallowed the neighboring island is reverberating with the inner tsunami about to swallow me?*

Her hands felt tired. She placed the drawing pad on her lap and kept her right hand over her left to rest a while. She looked at those hands, first the backs and then the fronts and palms. She examined them as if they belonged to someone else, as if she had just discovered them. What flexibility, dexterity and power! What beautiful artworks they had assisted her to conjure on paper! She gazed at them with new respect, as if they had been given to her as an anonymous gift. She had never really paid any attention to them before, never admired them the way she appreciated them now.

She thought of her hands washing her, styling her hair, opening and shutting doors and windows for her. How many meals had they prepared, how many dishes had they washed, how many vegetables peeled, flowers picked, clothing stitched? Her hands had helped her create her surrounding reality. Whatever else had happened was just a dream.

Priya felt she was creating her finest work by deftly applying each line, making an outline here, shading with quick strokes there, and conjuring up innumerable paths with the sharp pencil tip. Her gaze focused on each line— each passing cloud, flying bird, open gate, path leading toward infinity. The scene had developed under her hand, an enticing and mysterious landscape perfect in each stroke. The finest... and her last.

For the last fifty-eight years she had used her hands for everything she did. Like faithful attendants they had waited to serve her. In a way, her life depended on her hands, and on her feet and legs and head and—oh God, she had never given attention to any part of her body! She had neglected it when healthy. Now when it was failing, suddenly she had woken to its usefulness and almost sacral beauty. Had her body tried to communicate with her all these years? Priya had never listened.

She rationalized that no one was to be blamed. It was what it was. And all this was going to end soon. No meals to cook, no doors to open or close, no flowers to pick, no art to be made, no music to hear.

Priya began to cry. The salty tears rolled softly down her face and fell on her hands resting on the sketchpad in her lap. Her fingers twitched. She wiped the wetness under her eyes. Crying was not going to cure her fate. She took another look at the drawing. There was something wrong. To fix it she would have to erase the bamboo gate. What a shame! She stared intently at the beautiful depiction. The flaw glared at her. Why had she not noticed it before? She inhaled and exhaled heavily.

"What are you thinking?" Manohar asked. He leaned against her chair and saw her erasing the gate, then he walked to the window and opened it. "Calm before the storm."

"Can a tsunami devastate our island the way it sank the small one?"

"Who knows! We're not out of it yet."

"What do you think will happen when it comes?" she asked.

"No one knows for sure what happened to the small island, or what it will do to this one if the storm reaches here."

"Why couldn't we stop it before it got this far and this big?"

"Nobody knows how it comes, when it comes, who gets it, what lands it affects."

Through the window, a cool breeze brought the smell of jasmine and roses and cut grass into the room. She sighed. The thought, that her illness wasn't very different from the tsunami that had gulped down the small island, passed her mind.

Priya continued to erase what she had earlier drawn with force and confidence. Her spectacles flashed in the darkness of summer night. Through the silence she heard crickets and mosquitoes. She cocked her neck to listen.

What would she hear when she could no longer listen? They say sound keeps this world and the next world connected. Perhaps all the wisdom of the world religions was written or spoken to make us feel less fearful in the face of death, to give us courage and hope. Was it possible that tomorrow the doctor would call and say it was all a big mix up? *I'll get over it in a few months. I'll be loving my husband, opening doors, stirring curries, peeling oranges, and arranging flowers.* Perhaps the diagnosis of two different doctors was wrong. They could call and say she was going to be all right. *"How foolish," I'll say— all that worry. I will laugh and run to my husband and give him the news. Together we'll chuckle and say, "What were we so afraid of?"*

Wishful thinking! "Foolish," she said to herself, bending her head to look at the motion of her pencil, then busied herself with drawing.

Manohar came from the kitchen to see how she had changed the image. She looked up and they smiled at each other.

Two clashing stones in water had replaced the bamboo gate. The erased lines were still visible, a palimpsest of her floating thoughts, the mental clouds. She could hear her own breathing. Long and deep inhales and exhales relaxed her.

From that very moment she was not going to think why it happened to her. And she should never think that the tsunami would ever come to the island they so loved.

What followed the next day happened in slow motion. Gateways and pathways surfaced and sank in Priya's drawing. Clouds floated in, birds appeared and disappeared in the clouds. The gourd head of Manohar's sitar cracked. Its wires broke, the ones that once made sweet sounds. Darkness engulfed the drawn landscape. Beautiful handiwork, so painstakingly done, dissolved, going back to where it came from. Priya was in one dimension, Manohar in another. He couldn't know what was happening to her. One had no way of knowing what was happening to the other.

Priya laid on their bed and he was seated at its edge.

"Come, my husband. Come closer to me. Sit beside me. Hold my hand, hold me, kiss me."

He did what she wanted. He kissed her once, then again and again—on her cheeks and on her lips. Priya looked into his eyes, her gaze lingering at his familiar face, each slope and turn and wrinkle.

"I have always loved you but never as much as I love you at this moment," she said. "Yet my time here has ended. I selfishly wish I did not have to leave you alone. Believe me, if this parting—this separation—was under my control, I would stay, wait for you. If we had children, I would be content leaving you in their nourishing, protective hands, but you have friends and some family. Take good care of yourself."

Tears dripped down Priya's temples. Manohar's eyes had not welled up because even now he was not ready to accept her death the way she had. She had used up all the breath left in her deteriorating body. Now her breathing changed. It became deliberate, purposeful, severe. Priya pushed herself further than ever before. She worked at achieving, reaching, completing.

Then she closed her eyes, smiled and said, "Oh, wow!" Her last breath came as she saw herself walking through the landscape she had created. She passed through the clashing stones toward the unknown distant destination. She sighed one last time and murmured, "Oh, wow."

THE HI-FI NEEDLE

Gail Oare

My daughter asks me how it works—
How deep that strange drill must dig
to waken melodies hanging from
the roof of the black cave.

Just a touch, I say, like a crane's beak
against its reflection on a brittle lake.
One tap and everything with wings
flies up from the grasses singing.

It's spellbinding. Watch how
the ridges spin away the seconds,
how the needle skips over
the warped and worn surface
of your favorite songs,
how the old chords sizzle
like butter in a hot skillet
and quickly melt away.

But, I say, you can learn to raise
the levered arm from the noise
and lower it again and again
in endless benediction.

You can go back
to when your dreams
are diamond sharp and
your future lifting,
and bring it to rest once more
where the dinner table's set and you,
young and distracted, arrive
as everything's dishing up.

And as memories settle down
as gently as a folded napkin,
you can hear the soft staccato
of your mother's voice—
Elbows, chew slowly,
dishes to the sink, homework—
a song that goes on and on.

THE ELEPHANT IN THE ROOM

Deborah Vita

For many, the word love brings to mind visions of unicorns and rainbows, hearts and balloons, and bunnies nuzzling each other on greeting cards. Elephant images do not usually make it to the Valentine card section of the store.

Yet, oddly enough, elephants are among the most exuberantly expressive of creatures. Joy, anger, grief, compassion, love... the finest emotions reside within these hulking masses.

The elephant became my quiet nemesis. Hanging in the air, constantly butting into my life and turning things upside down. In nature, the gentle giant may express love for its offspring and mates in a big way. But in my life, the elephant would force me to acknowledge its presence, grabbing the tusks and shaking, sending it away, never to intrude again.

Elephants love in a big way, but for humans, this tiny four-letter word impacts our lives differently. Songs are written about it, poems, stories, and volumes of books offer guidance on how to get it, keep it, change or mold it to fit your life. We long for it, and yet when we finally have it...

we don't always appreciate or value it. And yes, at times, we even hate love. Or, at least, I have.

Love is different for me now that I'm older. At this age, sexy means watching my husband in baggy shorts, black socks and a ripped T-shirt vacuuming the living room. The hands I adored touching me now look attractive holding a plumber's wrench. We used to ride snowmobiles through five-foot drifts, sun in our eyes, surrounded by nature, then stop for a drink at a local bar. Now, I have coffee on the deck and he rides the mower.

When I think of the romantic love I felt as a teenager and as a young wife, I'm overwhelmed by the memory of how painful and beautiful it was at the same time. There was a physical attraction, but what I seem to remember the most was the fear. Fear of failing at marriage or motherhood, or not being good enough for someone to truly love me. Love wasn't always a pleasant experience then, but I accepted what I had and convinced myself it was "good enough."

Later in life, good enough began to take a toll. Love was nowhere to be found except in the eyes of my toddler boy. Marital love disintegrated with alcoholism taking over my husband's life. Eventually, it would take his life, literally. I remember my son asking me years later why I never cried at his father's funeral. Despite all the disappointments and anger and broken promises, I never spoke disparagingly about his dad. I did love the man in the beginning but his choices and the disease were not something either of us could survive.

When he passed, love was no longer there. Not loving him anymore, I think, was necessary for my survival.

Interestingly, even though love was gone, so was the hate. I no longer hated him for the man he'd become. I was more or less numb of any feelings except for compassion and sorrow for his mother who was now left alone with only me and her grandson. But, as much as I hated to admit it, love for the man was no longer existent. And that was okay with me. I didn't have guilt because I was satisfied I had done everything possible to make things better, but I had grown enough to know when to make a change.

After he died, I was fine being unattached, even though he had sent us into bankruptcy, and I had to move in with my parents in order to provide a safe, stable home for my son. I experienced love from my parents in a whole new way. It didn't matter that I was an adult now. My dad protected me and my mother welcomed me. Both assumed their roles as grandparents, giving love to my son and me in a way that saved us.

It was around this time I learned the importance of loving to laugh. I began to write. Although I loved to read just about any type of fiction, I couldn't easily write it. I could write funny. And I learned to love funny. It is how I've survived all this time.

Then, years later, I fell in love again, this time I believed for real. For a man whose faults are legion. Let's just get that out of the way first. I didn't fall in love with perfection but I was no longer settling for good enough. And that was hard for a lot of people to understand because, on the outside, he was not outstanding second-husband material, either. But for me, something was different with him. Something that made me feel safe, protected. A familiarity was there which to this day I cannot explain. I'm not sure I believe in soul mates but from the first time we met, I was certain I knew him. From before. From somewhere. I thought maybe we had seen each other, living in the same neighborhood or attending the same school. Eventually I discovered he grew up in an entirely different part of town.

Our early relationship went through dips and curves and rebounds but somehow circumstances placed us back in the same part of the universe, and each time I learned something new about him and me. We eventually moved in together at a particularly difficult time in my life. My mother had cancer and since my father had passed away years before from the same disease, we became a caregiving team. Somehow we became stronger together.

After my mother passed, we decided to marry since we jokingly admitted it appeared, after all the pain and changes we both experienced through her illness, we were stuck with each other. And I was happy. I felt I'd finally found my forever love.

Or so I thought.

After 15 years of marriage, something came between us that I never could have seen coming and it shook me to my core.

You can never truly be prepared in a marriage for the discovery of an affair.

I often wondered if I had found out my first husband had cheated on me, would I have had the same reaction, which was an almost complete nervous breakdown. This second time was supposed to be different. I felt this relationship was the real deal, the solid one, the one with no fear, where I could trust this person with my life.

His betrayal was so complete and precise, it struck me dead in the center of my very soul, nearly destroying me.

After months of fights and long silences, endless nights of tears to the point of exhaustion, hopelessness filled the air and lingered like smoke from an explosion. The very air I was trying to breathe felt poisonous.

I decided I needed to be alone and away from the situation for a while. I drove west to Arizona to visit my son and eventually moved there on my own. Two thousand miles alone in a car for four days with just your cat for company makes you realize a lot of new stuff about yourself. I was 55 years old and had never lived alone. In a new state, surrounded by cactus, sand, mountains and scorching heat I found I might actually learn to like myself. I remember crossing the state line into New Mexico and feeling a new freedom. My shoulders felt lighter. My head was clear for the first time in a long while. And for some irrational reason, I was not afraid.

I rented a small house in a retirement community—a blessing and a curse. Retired people have a lot of time on their hands which, at least in this particular neighborhood, made them very nosy. I just wasn't willing to share my entire life's story with people I had just met at breakfast. And, oddly enough, I really enjoyed my time alone. Talking was not something I required. I needed to just be with myself. I liked the silence.

During this time, communications with my husband were strained and infrequent. We spoke when necessary to discuss finances, or something about our adult children.

At times, the phone conversations devolved into fighting as if we were in the same room and not separated by almost a dozen state lines.

Then, somehow, our conversations became more focused. More truths were shared by us both. I could sense not so much a change in our interaction, but more of something familiar reappearing. Hearing his voice brought me a sense of comfort I had forgotten. There would be silence, reluctance to end the call. I could hear his breathing, visualize his chest moving. I felt something different. I felt hope returning, maybe love, and as my lease came to an end, I also returned home.

Things were not all rainbows and unicorns. Not that I expected a kumbaya moment soon after walking in the door. In fact, I fell into a sort of depression that took me a long time to recognize. Many of the problems we'd experienced before I left were still there, staring me in the face.

Then, it happened. One of those moments where you're sort of outside of your body, talking to yourself, maybe hitting yourself upside of the head with an imaginary rolled up newspaper. When the heavens open up and the angels sing, and the painfully obvious makes its presence known.

That day, I sat staring in my living room, when a voice in my head said, *If you do not get help, this thing is going to end very badly. The kind of badly that ends up on the six o'clock news.* I was pretty sure I wasn't going to hurt myself, but the anger I felt inside scared me.

The woman involved in the affair was still around, not physically, but in the neighborhood, so to speak. The elephant in the room was still present. I liked that metaphor because I enjoyed picturing her as an elephant. I never hated another human being as much as I hated her.

I used to tell myself that if I ever saw her on the road, I would run her over, set her on fire, then back up and run over her again. Not something I'm proud of admitting. Of course, it was all a fantasy in my head. Nevertheless, now I would like to state, for the record, that I wish her no harm. Otherwise if anything happens, I could be a prime suspect.

The separation did not solve the problem nor did it answer any questions. Worrying if he was still involved with this person was exhausting. And I knew it was time to fish or cut bait. I announced with as much courage as I could that if he would be happier, then he should just go be with her. I wouldn't stop him. I loved him, but my time away had taught me that it was more important to love myself first than it was to love him. Settling for good enough would not work this time.

Yet, even when presented with that option—a clear and concise way out—he did not leave.

I did not leave.

I hated to admit it, but I still loved him. I believed he still loved me. Otherwise, he would have been gone by now. At least I hoped that was true. But if I was to stay in this relationship, I needed help learning how to live with the past, accepting the present and shaping the future so that love would take on a new meaning.

That day in my living room, I realized since my return I was more unhappy than before I left because of my decision to stay in the marriage. I needed to learn that forgiving is not forgetting and the two emotions can coexist. I needed to get help. I needed to learn how to do that while keeping my sanity, controlling the anger and stopping research on how to effectively use a flame thrower from a moving car.

After three years in therapy, I'm not totally ashamed to admit I still meet with my counselor, just less frequently. I've learned more about my husband simply by talking about him to another person. He's never once stepped into an appointment with me, yet somehow he has changed for the better without the benefit of face-to-face therapy. It's not been easy. Many times, I felt I was doing all the work and he was just putting up roadblocks impeding any progress we might make toward a more healthy relationship.

My therapist has told me a hundred times we all have different prescriptions in our "life glasses"—how each of us sees life is different depending on how we were raised, what our parents did to encourage us, or not, and how they expressed their love for us, or not. Many experiences make up our prescription but how we handle being loved and giving love truly makes us the person we become later in life.

Talking with a professional made me realize something vitally important. I hadn't made another bad husband choice. I'd simply learned his prescription glasses were different. Growing up he didn't learn to express love in the traditional way, and in order to keep my sanity, I've learned to accept that.

He's never going to read a book about love or relationships. He's a volunteer firefighter and paramedic who loves hunting and fishing and watching car shows and the *Three Stooges*. He builds things and buys power tools and understands how an electrical panel works. Growing up, the prescription in his glasses must not have allowed him to see how a hug or a compliment or giving a gift at Christmas can be an expression of love.

Yet, every year he puts on a Santa suit and transforms into someone I do not recognize. He visits children at the local hospital and rides the fire truck through the neighborhood giving out candy.

He won't easily admit family is the most important thing to him. Seeing him with his grandchildren proves that beneath that gruff, hard exterior lies a bear eating a bag of marshmallows watching *Sesame Street*.

He passes the "animals know a good person test" with flying colors. My best friend's dog practically leaped into his arms when he came into the room. She announced casually, "That's weird. She doesn't really like men." Our cat runs to the door to meet him at the end of the day and plops in his lap as soon as he sits down. Animals know.

I've learned to feel love for him in a different way, but also compassion and empathy because I realize his childhood must have been difficult. Even though he doesn't talk about it, I know there is something hidden inside which I'm quite sure he will never share.

Coming back to someone who has betrayed you in such a deep way is hard for many to understand. It may seem as if I'm accepting his behavior and making excuses for it. I'll admit at times, I didn't understand it myself. Going back may sound like settling for less. But learning why a person behaves in a certain way can make all the difference. Our relationship has grown in ways that maybe others who have not experienced an affair cannot appreciate.

The most important thing I've learned is that even though his outlook on love is a bit skewed from mine, deep down he is a good man. Otherwise I would not have come back. Something my inner voice recognized told me not to give up on him.

Admitting I needed help that day made all the difference. While seeking guidance, I thought I was learning how to love him better, or make him love me differently. I realize now that was not the entire point. Seeking counseling taught me how to forgive and learn to love myself. Loving and forgiving someone else means much more if you can achieve that first.

Thank God for that elephant in the room. Without that, who knows where I'd be?

To My Husband

Madhu Bazaz Wangu

I dive my face into your chest
as someone thirsty plunges into a stream.
In that infinite expanse I smell the scents of Old Spice
and cigarettes.
Let me inhale you with the enthralling sweetness
of your kiss.
Let me feel your touch and reminisce us
growing old together.

When I met you, I dreamt of an ideal life.
Your presence inspired my visions of vast oceans,
clouds carrying us to enchanted lands
where skies are always blue,
and spring is forever.

In your eyes I glimpsed our lush life together
from budding love to adoring bloom,
from unfolding mystery to intoxicating wine.
We delighted in our children,
in their innocence and intelligence.
In loving them and in caressing you,
I forget our weariness and worries!

Only if you could know how much I love you.
How empty I feel in your absence.
And how my soul soars in your presence.

Though no longer young, let's kiss and caress.
Let me rest my head on your graying chest to let you know
that all my dreams have come true.

WHAT IS LOVE?

S. M. Kraftchak

As if I wasn't anxious enough to be the only thirty-something in the room, I was forced to pardon and excuse my way across the middle row of the auditorium to the center, the last available seat. It wasn't just an age thing, being surrounded by twenty-somethings, it was... something I couldn't put into words. It was silly. There was no reasonable explanation for my reticence.

I had avoided taking this class, Psychology of Biology, until my final semester because of him. It had been nearly a year since I collided on the quad with the professor who taught it. Imagine the stereotypical scene of books and papers flying everywhere when two people lost in their own worlds collide, followed by harried apologies on my part as we both scrambled to collect and sort out our mingled belongings.

At first, he was in quite the snit until I handed him his last folder of notes, looking like an overstuffed taco, and our eyes met. He suddenly stopped and just stared, open mouthed, at my face. I offered a few more "I really am so sorry" but when he did nothing but stare, I mumbled, "Have a nice day," and ran for my car without looking back.

The next day I was thoroughly embarrassed to have been gaggled by a dozen much younger female students congratulating me on my strategy to get the attention of the most eligible, and best-looking man on campus, even if he was known to be one of the toughest professors. I dismissed their nonsense and thought little more about it, until now.

I startled when the door above and behind us at the top of the auditorium clacked shut. Nearly a hundred sets of eyes, except mine, turned to see Dr. Albert Dennis pause at the top of the stairs. His sonorous voice filled the lecture hall, probably melting half the female hearts in the room.

"We can neither see nor touch love, yet it makes us crave this emotion—a deep-seated need for fulfilment of a connection, a sense of completion, a wholeness that only love can bring." He descended the steep steps one by one, and paused at the end of my row. I could see him out of the corner of my eye, but concentrated on my composition book, scribbling since my mind wouldn't focus on anything but his words.

"In its simplest form, love is a myriad of biological responses that defy logic and drive reason from the sane, compelling us to search for its capriciousness though fleeting, one sided, or even lost."

I squirmed in my seat, trapped. If I tried to escape, I'd only draw attention to myself or make a scene. I felt Dr. Dennis's words spin through the air like an untied balloon set free before they found their target, hitting me square in the chest.

He continued walking. "Love is an instinctive or intuitive feeling. It manifests as an unreasonable individual bias and preference. It is a connection, whether to another person, an animal, or on occasion an inanimate object. It sends our hearts soaring with joy, flooding our biological system with the chemicals dopamine and oxytocin that make our hearts race, creating a euphoria, and heightening sensitivity to touch when the focus of our love appears..." He paused when he reached the podium on stage, produced a file folder with papers sticking out of it in helter-skelter fashion, made a great show of organizing them into a neat pile and placed them flat before he looked up at me. "Or flings us into a pit of despair when love is lost."

I swallowed the lump in my throat, tugged at my scarf, and blinked hard to stop my eyes from burning. Was he some kind of stalker? I wrote in my notebook: *Why is he doing this? He can't be a stalker. We only met once. How can I...?*

He stepped to the side of his podium and leaned on an elbow as he scanned the sea of students. "Mother's love is the first we experience. The warm tender instinctive connection happens when eyes connect and focus, imprinting a face in the mind. This face, and those we connect with Mother and Father, siblings, and caregivers, become our daily sustenance of love and its joy, teaching our bodies and minds to desire this satisfying emotion. But even more intense than sight is the connection we find through Mother's touch—the pleasantness of a caress, the warmth of skin against skin, or the pleasing combination of warmth and touch in a kiss."

While I was older than everyone else in the room, I certainly wasn't old enough to be his mother. How Oedipal, connecting a mother's love with desire. But we'd never touched and I couldn't imagine kissing... I quickly bit my lower lip when I found my mouth opening in response to his words. Why was he so... so mesmerizing? This wasn't like me at all.

He turned and sauntered stage left with his hands clasped behind him, seeming to talk to his brown Oxfords as if no one else were in the room. "While our experiences of love are as individual as we are, we slowly learn to reach beyond Mother's love to find satisfaction with others, though perhaps less powerful it is nonetheless vital to our well-being. She introduces us to grandparents, friends, and teachers with whom we quickly connect and learn a different level of what pleases us, or not. We seek out those who trigger pleasant degrees of love and steadfast connections, creating bonds that cross barriers and span a lifetime." He turned as if remembering he had an audience.

I felt his eyes connect with mine, sucking the air from my lungs.

"But instinctively we seek out an individual, one who triggers the most fulfilling and intense biological response, molded by our life's experience and preferences. It is that fleeting moment," he raised just one finger, "when we defy all logic that we find our mate, the person who causes our heart to race, our body to tremble with the anticipation of being complete, and fills our hearts with love."

One of the young starry-eyed co-eds raised her hand.

"Yes, Cali? Please stand so everyone can hear you."

I cringed behind my hand and thought, *Oh my God! He knows everyone's name? How can he possibly...? Don't be silly. She must have been in one of his other classes.*

Cali stood, adjusted her hair and shirt, and grinned like she'd just won an award. "Why then, Professor, if love is so simple and basic, do we find so much 'heartache' in the world? We hear about lost love, falling out of love, or unrequited love."

He motioned her to sit. "Excellent question and there is no quantifiable answer. Perhaps it is a trick of our biology. Our embedded memory is so desperate to match that perfect moment of pure love..." I peeked from behind my hand to see him squinting at his nearly pinched fingers that emphasized his words. "...that it allows our minds to believe we have correctly assayed the quality and quantity of an emotional connection, and believe we are fulfilled, convincing us we are complete. But then in our capricious need for the most, the best, the fullest experience of our memory of love, we begin to doubt we have evaluated properly. Our attentions are divided and we lose focus of what we have learned brings the purest joy of love. Or, tragically, when our perfect connection ceases to exist, we are flooded not with love, but the emptiness and lack of love, that carefully refined connection that filled us with so much joy."

I sat back and covered my mouth, swallowing to keep my tears at bay. How could I have been so oblivious? So afraid? Ten years ago, I'd closed myself off to any relationship, afraid to feel after my "first true love" devastated me when he told me he could feel nothing for me if refused to return his love, which to him meant going all the way. Tears rolled down my cheeks as I returned Professor Dennis's gaze.

He broke our connection after perhaps fifteen seconds, although it seemed like an eternity to me, and scanned the rest of the class. "So does all this reasoning that love is simple biology in its innumerable forms of complexity change our needs or desires? No. Love is, at its finest, an instinctive connection to the world and an intuitive completion of us." He laser-eyed every student in the hall. "I see by your expressions I have given you a lot to think about. Instead of embarrassing you by asking you to share your feelings in such a public forum, I want everyone to contemplate: Is love a biological response or a construct of the mind? Write a five-page essay supporting your opinion." There was a collective groan. "That will be due at the beginning of next session. Class dismissed."

Discussion filled the room as the thwack of seats popping up made conversation unintelligible. I remained seated, absent-mindedly drawing intricate patterns like Celtic designs—a reflection of my chaotic emotions—in my notebook.

Suddenly aware everyone else had left, I noted solitary footsteps ascending the stairs. I focused on my paper, surprised to find I had written: *I love you too.*

"Ms. Clayton. Are you well?" Professor Dennis walked toward me, one row down.

I snapped my composition book shut and dropped it into my briefcase.

"Professor Dennis, yes. Why do you ask?"

He raised his eyebrows and looked down at his feet again, as if he wished there were a few stones to kick, but there weren't so he eased onto the arm of one of the seats. I felt awkward like he was sitting at my feet adoring me.

"I don't intend to make you feel uncomfortable, but you seemed a bit upset. Perhaps it's because of our previous encounter? Can you forgive me for not properly apologizing?"

I felt a flush of heat in my cheeks when I remembered his expression from that day. "Oh... no. No apology needed." I waved my hand. "Don't worry about it. As I recall, it was me who ran into you." I grabbed my purse and tucked away my pen rather than clicking it nervously, also so I didn't have to meet his eyes.

"I do need to apologize. Would you permit me to do so properly over maybe a cup of Oolong tea at the Snak and Yak?"

How did he know my favorite tea? I adjusted the shoulder strap on my purse and stood. "There's no need for that. Besides, others might get the wrong idea that we, a student and a professor, are dating, and that would cause all kinds of trouble for both of us, but thank you." I started to walk away.

"Is it a wrong idea? Would you like to date me?" he said.

I turned back to see he now stood with his hands buried in the pockets of his khaki pants, his face pinched with worry. "Are you trying to create some kind of experiment to prove the point of your lecture?"

"So, you were listening."

I didn't trust my voice so I nodded.

"It's no experiment. It's the truth and I think you know it."

I took a shuddering breath to control my rising emotions and nodded again.

"We can't get in trouble."

I answered him with a confused look and, "Excuse me?"

"You aren't enrolled in my class anymore."

"But I need this credit to graduate!"

He snickered and shrugged. "Nope. There was an error on your transcripts. I had your advisor double-check. You need the other two courses you're taking but not this one."

"Really?" I felt my heart soar unexpectedly when I realized I could acknowledge the feelings for this man that I'd secluded away.

"Really. You aren't my student, so there can be no impropriety."

I couldn't control my tears as I looked at my sandals, trying to figure out where we went from here. I looked up, wiping away my tears as I walked back to him and asked, "Can I still write the essay?"

He grinned like he'd won a prize. "How about we talk about it over tea, instead, at my apartment?"

I leaned forward cautiously and closed my eyes as he leaned toward me. Our lips barely touched and I pulled away. "I'd like that."

WHEN FOOD IS LOVE

Ramona DeFelice Long

My grandmother loved coconut. Grom made coconut cake, coconut custard pie, ambrosia with coconut, and once a year, mountains of coconut pralines to bag and give as Christmas presents. By the time I was old enough to remember, she had too many grandchildren for individual presents. A bag of coconut pralines was her gift. If I'd had to choose between a new Barbie or a bag of coconut pralines, I'm not sure...

There was one caveat: you had to pick up the bag from her house, in person. If you didn't visit Grom's house on Christmas Day—no pralines for you!

Making pralines was a production requiring cutting up brown paper bags to cover the kitchen counters, and using a handmade cast iron pot deep enough to boil sugar but small enough that she could carry it and spoon out drop cookies. Because boiling sugar was dangerous, no one was allowed in the kitchen on praline-making day, which had to be cool and dry or the pralines would not set correctly.

I volunteered to be her helper because I loved spending time with Grom, especially one on one, and because I love coconut pralines, especially when they are still warm and the sugar has not yet cooled and crystallized.

My grandmother did not speak much English, and she never recorded any of her recipes in her native Cajun French. Luckily, just about every Southern food cookbook shares a recipe for coconut pralines.

Another of my grandmother's original recipes was a less sweet treat, perfect with a cup of coffee. Grom's tea cakes were squares or rectangles or whatever shape she felt like cutting that day. Tea cakes were soft and warm, dusty with flour, light but hearty if you ate enough of them.

Coconut pralines were my favorite, but my mom loved the tea cakes. Like every other recipe of Grom's, this one was never recorded. Unfortunately, they're not a staple in Southern cookbooks, so a few years after Grom passed away, my mother decided to recreate the recipe. My dad was a willing taste tester. It took many, many batches to reach a recipe that tasted like Grom's.

Mom's Version of Grom's Tea Cakes

Ingredients

2 sticks butter
2 c sugar
4 eggs
2 tsp. baking powder
½ tsp. baking soda
½ tsp. salt
1 tsp. vanilla
¼ c milk
≈7 c all-purpose flour

Directions

Heat oven to 375°. Cream butter and sugar. Add in eggs one at a time, stirring each one in. Sift dry ingredients with one cup of flour. Mix well. Add milk and vanilla. Add flour one cup at a time to proper consistency for rolling dough on floured surface.

Roll out dough to about a half-inch thickness. Cut into shapes about 2" x 2". Bake on cookie sheet (sprayed with Pam) for 13-15 minutes until light tan. Store in airtight container.

RECIPE FOR LOVE

Adaptation of I Corinthians 13:4-13

Denise Weaver

Love is being patient with one another, even with those who hold up the line while precisely folding their dollar bills before placing in their wallets, and those who cut you off in traffic.

Love is living, showing, feeling kindness, even when in a hurry, even when on the receiving end of an unkind act, even when we don't feel like it.

Love is supporting and celebrating others, even when they receive the one thing you were desperately hoping for, possibly a promotion, a book deal, a baby, a partner.

Love is showing humility and gratitude, showing mercy, giving justice, seeking and honoring truth. Even when it would be easier to join in or perpetuate, love will forgo hurtful gossip, ridiculous demands, accepting undeserved privilege, perpetuating untruth.

Love is understanding even when life's situations are not always fair. Love believes and hopes for better days and takes with grace what has to be in the moment.

Love is ongoing, not temporary, even when inconvenient. Love is real and abounds beyond lesser things.

Love is the greatest gift.

"Where have you been? I've missed you," she gushes. "Come in, come in. Have a seat. What can I get you? Coffee? Tea? A big ol' sandwich and glass of milk? Soup? A piece of pie? Oh, you have to be hungry. Let me fix you a plate. How have you been? What have you been up to? Are you happy? Do you need anything? Can I help you with anything?"

The deluge of words, all expressing concern and love and good wishes in various forms, only reinforces the welcome in her sparkling eyes. The farm kitchen is as warm as she is, and nearly as inviting. The old oak table that can seat twelve is always gleaming, ready to hold the next feast Aunt Vi's gnarled hands place upon it. Light streams in the almost spotless windows, and the floor creaks with the squeaky sound that is a reminder of the lovely wood floors under the hand-braided rugs.

Foodstuff starts to tumble out when the refrigerator door is opened, so plentiful are the building blocks of her inimitable style of hospitality. She would never run the risk of not being adequately prepared for an unexpected guest.

For anyone who stepped into Aunt Vi's kitchen, it was like reliving their best feeling of being at home. The penetrating but pleasant aroma of coffee brewing was ever present, as was the yeasty smell of freshly baked bread, and the sounds and odors of a pot of deliciousness simmering on the stovetop in preparation for that night's dinner.

Beyond the scents and sights and sounds of the ubiquitous hearty, rib-sticking, tantalizing foods she prepared, Aunt Vi welcomed anyone and everyone into her home as if they were the prodigal child returned. Her weathered face crinkled into a smile, her sinewy and tanned arms encircled the visitor with a hearty, warm embrace.

The passage about love from I Corinthians Chapter 13 is often read at weddings, but applies to so much more than marital love. Its instruction provides graspable concepts that, when applied, can lead to a life well-lived, a life of caring for everyone as a matter of routine.

Aunt Vi exemplified that type of grace and love. She gave without expecting anything in return. She was patient and kind. She didn't keep score. My wonderful aunt, by example, taught me acceptance, patience, hard work, good ethics, hospitality, joy in serving and giving, and genuine concern for others.

Love is, was, my Aunt Vi.

Aunt Vi's Spiced Coffee Bars

Ingredients

¼ cup softened butter or Crisco
1 cup brown sugar
1 egg
½ cup hot coffee
1½ cup sifted flour
¼ tsp. baking soda

½ tsp. salt
1 tsp. baking powder
½ tsp. cinnamon
½ cup raisins
½ cup chopped nuts

Plus 1 cup powdered sugar, and a small amount of butter and cream for icing

Directions

Cream together butter and brown sugar. Add egg and coffee. Mix. Sift together dry ingredients and stir into batter. Add raisins and nuts.

Spread batter in greased 9x13 pan. Bake for 18-20 minutes in a preheated 350° oven.

Frost while slightly warm. Cut into 24 squares.

Icing

Cream 1 cup powdered sugar with enough soft butter and cream to make a thin icing. Add ½ tsp. vanilla and ¼ tsp. salt. Spread on bars.

CONTRIBUTORS

LORRAINE DONOHUE BONZELET is a graduate of Stevens Institute of Technology, The Institute of Children's Literature, Children's Book Academy, and a long-time member of the Society of Children's Book Writers and Illustrators. A retired engineer, she is a picture book enthusiast and mindful writer. Lorraine has a non-fiction article and photographs published in *Boys' Quest* magazine, "Unusual Sports." She's also published in the Mindful Writers Retreat Anthologies, *Into the Woods* and *Over the River and Through the Woods*. Her two tabby cats rule her humble abode in Maryland while she satiates her wanderlust, traveling with her husband, daughters, and sister. Lorraine conjures up stories and poems while walking in nature, jogging, kayaking, and gardening. She has a knack for concocting delicious new recipes—and a love for plants—but she's never mixed the two to create a toxic potion... yet!

JENNIFER D. DIAMOND, MS/CCC-SLP, is a speech therapist/reading specialist turned writer. Diamond is an award-winning author of personal essays, short stories, and Young Adult Fiction. When not writing or hiking, she spends time on the water SUP boarding and boating with her husband, two college-aged kids, and rescue pup in the northeast corner of the Laurel Highlands in Pennsylvania. jenniferddiamondwriter.wordpress.com

Facebook @Jennifer.D.Diamond.writer
Instagram @jennifer_d_diamond_writer

ABIGAIL DRAKE has spent her life traveling the world and collecting stories wherever she visited. She is a book hoarder, a coffee drinker, a linguistics geek, and an eternal optimist. Abigail was awarded an honorable mention for her book *Love, Chocolate, and a Dog Named Al Capone* in the Writer's Digest Self-Published E-book Awards, 2019. She writes women's fiction and young adult fiction, and also enjoys blogging about the adventures of her mischievous Labrador retriever, Capone. www.abigaildrake.com.

JUDY ENGLAND-McCARTHY is a professional storyteller, author, and poet. She spoke at the National Storytelling Conference twice and one of her poems was presented in video format for "The Just Listening Project." Another poem won 1st place at Fanstory.com in 2020. Her work appears in anthologies of the Greater Lehigh Valley Writers Group and Mindful Writers Retreat Series. "Twas Midnight" and "Why, Oh Why, Did a Witch Swallow a Fly?" will be released later this year. Her first book *Amazing Petunia's Adventures* is being made into an animation and is available on Amazon. Beginwithastory.com

PHIL GIUNTA's novels include the paranormal mysteries *Testing the Prisoner*, *By Your Side*, and *Like Mother, Like Daughters.* His short stories appear in such anthologies as *A Plague of Shadows*, *Beach Nights*, *Beach Pulp*, the ReDeus mythology series, and the Middle of Eternity speculative fiction series, which he created and edited for Firebringer Press. As a member of the Greater Lehigh Valley Writers Group, Phil also penned stories and essays for *Write Here, Write Now*, *The Write Connections*, and *Rewriting the Past*, three of the group's annual anthologies. He is currently working on a science fiction novel while plotting his triumphant escape from corporate America where he has been imprisoned for over twenty-five years.

www.philgiunta.com, Facebook: @writerphilgiunta, Twitter: @philgiunta71

KIMBERLY KURTH GRAY was born and raised in Baltimore where she finds daily inspiration for her writing. The winner of the William F. Deeck-Malice Domestic 2009 Grant for Unpublished Writers and a 2017 Hruska Fellowship, she is a member of Sisters in Crime, Guppies, and Pennwriters. Her short stories have been published in Cat and Mouse Press and Level Best Anthologies. In addition to working on a historical novel and writing short stories, she appears monthly as The Detective's Daughter on the Wicked Cozy Authors blog.

Science fiction has been N.J. HAMMER's favorite genre since childhood. For this author, crafting an intriguing story is as important as building the essence of a unique world. Masters of classic science fiction, such as Arthur C. Clark, Isaac Asimov, Ray Bradbury and Gene Roddenberry are as much her heroes as the most contemporary masters of the craft. In addition to writing science fiction for adults and middle grade readers, to pay the bills she's sold encyclopedias, worked in retail sales, added up the numbers as an accountant, clicked the computer keys as an administrative assistant and has driven the rambling roads as a real estate agent. But she always comes back to the story. njhammerauthor.com

HILARY HAUCK is the author of *From Ashes to Song*, a historical novel about a young Italian musician seeking a new start in America. Her stories have also appeared in the Mindful Writers Retreat Series anthologies, the *Ekphrastic Review, Balloons Lit. Journal*, and the Telepoem Booth. Hilary moved to Italy from her native UK as a young adult, where she mastered the language, learned how to cook food she can no longer eat, and won a national karate championship. After meeting her husband, Hilary came to the US and drew inspiration from Pennsylvania coal history, which soon became the setting for her debut novel. She lives on a small patch of woods in rural Pennsylvania with her husband, one of their three adult children, a cat with a passion for laundry, and an oversized German shepherd called Hobbes—of the Calvin variety. www.hilaryhauck.com

As a writer who spends most of her time in other worlds with dragons, elves, and the occasional alien, SHARON M. KRAFTCHAK still enjoys sunrises on the beach, sunsets in the mountains and portraying Elizabeth Tudor. While she's published in seven short story anthologies, her passion is writing novels

RAMONA DeFELICE LONG (1959-2020) wrote fiction, creative nonfiction, personal essays, and prose poetry. Her work appeared in literary, regional, and juvenile publications, and she received artist fellowships and grants from the Pennsylvania State Arts Council, the Delaware Division of the Arts, the Virginia Center for Creative Arts, the Mid-Atlantic Arts Foundation, and the SCBWI. Her short story "Voices" was nominated for a Pushcart Prize in 2017, and in 2015, her artist journey was selected by the National Endowment for the Arts to represent Delaware on the United States of Arts map. Ramona was a transplanted Southerner living in Delaware. www.ramonadef.com.

MARYALICE MELI lives in Steelers/Pirates/Penguins country, aka Pittsburgh, PA, and has written nonfiction in past careers in education and journalism. She earned a master's degree in writing popular fiction at Seton Hill University. Now retired, she writes short and flash fiction, children's stories, middle-grade mysteries, and has begun reading all the books on her shelves designated *TBR when there's time*. She placed third in Pennwriters's 2014 short fiction contest and had two short stories published in Rehoboth Writers Guild anthologies. She's also been published online in Every Day Fiction, InfectiveINk, and Untied Shoelaces of the Mind.

AMY MORLEY is a former journalist turned reading specialist who spends her days surrounded by books, and her nights surrounded by Yorkshire Terriers. Born and raised in the Steel City of Pittsburgh, she settled north in the small, idyllic town of Grove City, on which the events from "Just Give It Seven Days" were loosely based. What started out as a no risk seven-day relationship led to marriage, seven years later, to writer Michael D. Morley.

However, this story never would have come to fruition if it wasn't for her eleven-year-old nephew, Arthur, who coached his Aunt Amy through the entire storytelling process. She is currently working on a sweet romance novel, and her work will be featured in *The Ninth Room*, a collection of poetry told through the collective minds of ten different authors, slated for release later in 2021. Facebook @AmyMorleyAuthor

GAIL OARE is retired from a career in science and educational publishing. After several years of producing training films, technical manuals, marketing materials and magazines, she was given the opportunity to establish a multimillion-dollar science publishing business for an international organization which she then directed for 25 years. A lifelong creative writer, she now concentrates on writing and publishing short stories and poetry and occasional science features. She began exploring haiku, senryu, haiga and haibun several years ago and more than 250 of her pieces have appeared in journals and anthologies. In her spare time, she is learning to play the Scottish smallpipes and has returned to her musical roots of guitar and English concertina.

Although KIM PIERSON has been writing stories since an unfortunate and hugely forgettable *Little Women* knock-off in the fourth grade, as an adult, she spent years practicing law and securing a Master's in library science prior to shifting her focus to writing full-time. She lives with her husband and four children just outside of Pittsburgh, where she bakes too much, reads even more, and continues to unapologetically cheer for the Wisconsin sports teams of her youth.

JAMES ROBINSON, JR. hails from Pittsburgh, PA. He has written both fiction and non-fiction. His first book, *Fighting the Effects of Gravity: A Bittersweet Journey into Middle Life*, is a humorous look at midlife filled with autobiographical anecdotes. *Gravity* won an Indie Book Award. His fiction consists of a three-book series chronicling the life of The Johnson Family. Mr. Robinson's book, *Death of a Shrinking Violet,* consists of thirteen humorous essays.

Award winning author Dr. LARRY SCHARDT is known for his presentations on success, leadership, motivation, happiness, and living with a great attitude. His passions are teaching, music, the outdoors, and people. As a professor at Penn State University for twenty-six years, his students tagged him as the best and most fun. Larry also captures his audience when he is a keynote speaker at conferences and retreats. He posts a daily motivational blog on Facebook where he brightens his audience with the beauty and positives of life. He encourages everyone to live with gratitude, thrive with gusto, and explore the world with a sense of wonder. Larry loves sharing joy, kindness, and secrets of success in his upcoming book *Success that Rocks.* He is a man who greets everyone with exuberance, the peace sign, and his favorite blessing, "Rock 'n' Roll!"
facebook.com/Larry.Schardt twitter.com/LarrySchardt

Bestselling author, KATHLEEN SHOOP, holds a PhD in reading education and has more than twenty years of experience in the classroom. She writes historical fiction, women's fiction, and romance. Shoop's novels have garnered various awards in the Independent Publisher Book Awards (IPPY), Eric Hoffer Book Awards, Indie Excellence Awards, Next Generation Indie Book Awards, Readers' Favorite, and the San Francisco Book Festival. Kathleen has been featured in *USA Today* and the *Writer's Guide to 2013*. Her work has appeared in *The Tribune-Review*, four *Chicken Soup for the Soul* books, and *Pittsburgh Parent* magazine. Kathleen coordinates Mindful Writing Retreats and is a regular presenter at conferences for writers. She lives in Oakmont, Pennsylvania, with her husband and two children. www.kshoop.com, Facebook @Kathleen Shoop.

DEMI STEVENS, CEO of Year of the Book Press, turns authors' writing dreams into successfully published books. She has personally assisted in the production of more than 300 titles by 130 authors, ranging from children's picture books to sizzling romance, award-winning mysteries, and bestselling business books. She holds degrees from West Virginia University, Capital, Northwestern, and Ohio State, and has served on the faculties of Ohio State and Delaware Valley University, and as Director of Paul Smith Library. Many call Demi the "Book Whisperer," but perhaps "Book Midwife" is more appropriate, because literary labor and delivery can be so painful. Each year she coaches a limited number of writers one-on-one through the entire drafting, editing, and publishing process. yotbpress.com

LISA VALLI, a Certified Financial Planner and Benefits Consultant, has been featured in *INC Magazine* and Who's Who of American Women for her professional achievements. But she also enjoys exercising her "right brain" by creating stories. She is a member of various writers' organizations and is currently working on a story inspired by her trips to nearby Deep Creek Lake, Maryland. She resides in Venetia, Pennsylvania, with her husband, two daughters and their little dog, Crosby (named after Sidney, of course).

DEBORAH VITA is a freelance writer living in southwestern Pennsylvania with her husband and two cats, Frasier and Niles. For nearly 25 years she worked in municipal government and retired as an assistant township manager. During that time, she handled public relations and education on municipal programs. She wore many "hats"—even dressing as Rudolph for Light Up Night. Her writing projects are inspired by finding humor in everyday experiences as well as her personal views on life as a wife, grandmother, and crazy cat lady. She is compiling her stories into a memoir celebrating laughter as the most important tool to living a happy life.

Founder of the Mindful Writers Groups and Retreats, MADHU BAZAZ WANGU's skillful Writing Meditation Practice combines meditation, journaling, walking, and reading. Dr. Wangu is a multi-award-winning author whose works have won Writer's Digest, Readers Favorite, Indie Excellence, Next Generation Indie Book, and TAZ awards. She is also the Pennwriters 2020 Meritorious Award winner. Dr. Wangu serves as a board member for

Books Bridge Hope which promotes reading, writing, and literacy to the community living in shelters and on streets. She is a frequent workshop presenter at Pennwriters Annual Conferences and was a featured author for Beaver County Book Fest in 2017. Her inspiring CDs *Meditations for Mindful Writers I, II & III* help cultivate focus, increase flow and productivity. Practice with her at Online Mindful Writers Group at: tinyurl.com/MindfulWriters

DENISE WEAVER is a freelance writer, a *summa cum laude* graduate of the University of Pittsburgh, and a former library director. With more than 200 published articles in local and regional magazines, she particularly enjoys researching and writing about food, nature, and personality profiles. She serves as copy editor and reader for *Hippocampus Magazine* and is a co-founder of the Festival of Books for the Alleghenies. Denise enjoys writing, photography, cooking, and traveling, and once performed on stage at Carnegie Hall. She lives in the beautiful Laurel Highlands of Pennsylvania.

MICHELE SAVAUNAH ZIRKLE, MA, PhD, is a published author, high school teacher and holistic energy practitioner who enjoys sharing innovative ways to break through writing barriers and to live a creative life. She is the author of *Rain No Evil*. In addition to hosting "Life Speaks," on Appalachian Independent Radio, Michele leads meditations and healing events, inspiring partici-pants to live with passion and purpose. Her short stories have appeared in *Mountain Ink Literary Journal* and vignettes in *The Journal of Health* and *Human Experience*. She presents writing workshops for West

Virginia Writer's Inc. and Northern Appalachia Writer's Conferences. She is a graduate of Concord University, Marshall Graduate School and The Institute of Metaphysical Humanistic Science.

www.michelezirkle.com Facebook @ZirksQuirks

CPSIA information can be obtained
at www.ICGtesting.com
Printed in the USA
BVHW072349021222
653360BV00001B/34